Praise for *Letti*

"A poignant treatise on the tricks of m[...]
loops, and knots across generations, [...]
read and a cathartic one. With a sense of immediacy that extends both to the
present and the past, Brader deftly puts an arm around the reader and brings
them along on her journey toward discovering the truth about her art forger
uncle—and to reconcile, in the end, how truth and the truths we tell ourselves
rarely run smoothly together."

—**Steph Post, author of** *Miraculum* **and** *Lightwood*

"Teresa Tumminello Brader expertly weaves a tale of both fiction and nonfiction
in this riveting account of a niece's discovery of a deeply hidden family secret.
As Brader herself says: 'memory is unreliable; it might as well be fiction.' But
in her exploratory and observant hands, we are swept along in her seeking to
understand the dark underbelly of her family heritage, and the conflicting legacy
of creative talent and mental illness, played out in the yin/yang of success versus
appropriation and fraud. Brava to Brader for breathing 'air and light' into this
largely unknown crime story. In doing so, she also shines an important spotlight
on the victim, folk artist Clementine Hunter. A powerful hybrid memoir that
is both tribute and indictment."

—**Tara Lynn Masih, author of** *How We Disappear*

"When life hands you an art forger for an uncle, you have no choice but to write
this wonderful book. Teresa Tumminello Brader's memoir is simultaneously an
absorbing page-turner and a deep, moral investigation into family, set against
the richly imagined world that was the New Orleans of her ancestors. So much
depends on that double-shotgun house on Plum Street. Written with generosity and warmth toward flawed people, this book lights its curious eye on the
tension between art and artifice, how we are made by our circumstances, and
what happens when the drive to create goes awry. An altogether splendid saga
of family secrets, unraveling over time."

—**Constance Adler, author of**
My Bayou: New Orleans Through the Eyes of a Lover

"Teresa Tumminello Brader is a born storyteller burdened by a dark and long-
hidden family secret. In search of the truth, she pieces together facts that reveal
an infamous art forger and con man living next door to her grandparents: her
brilliant, troubled uncle. What a fascinating tale to bring so bravely out into
the light of day."

—**Pia Z. Ehrhardt, author of** *Famous Fathers & Other Stories*

LETTING IN
AIR AND LIGHT

LETTING IN
AIR AND LIGHT

A MEMOIR

TERESA
TUMMINELLO BRADER

BELLE
POINT
PRESS

Fort Smith, Arkansas

LETTING IN AIR AND LIGHT

Cover image (and p. iv): detail of Van Gogh,
Green Wheat Fields, Auvers (1890);
window elements via rawpixel.
Author photo by Christy Lorio

Edited by Casie Dodd
Design & typography by Belle Point Press

Belle Point Press LLC
Fort Smith, Arkansas
bellepointpress.com
editor@bellepointpress.com

Find Belle Point Press
on Facebook,
Twitter (@BellePointPress),
and Instagram (@bellepointpress)

Printed in the United States of America

27 26 25 24 23   1 2 3 4 5

Library of Congress Control Number: 2023944465

ISBN: 978-1-960215-03-1

LIAL/BPP17

For Rhea, Mage, and our single shotgun house
on Baudin Street

Contents

Preface

LETTING IN AIR AND LIGHT is my story of William Toye, a convicted art forger and my uncle. Born in New Orleans, Louisiana, in 1931, he was my mother's older brother. She was the second child, born in 1938. I believe my grandmother suffered several miscarriages between their births, but they weren't much spoken of. Also not spoken of was Uncle Bill's arrest in 1974 for the selling of his forgeries of the work of Clementine Hunter.

Clementine Hunter was a self-taught and prolific Black artist from the Cane River region of Louisiana.[1] For more than forty years, she painted narrative pictures of northwestern Louisiana plantation life, as well as still-lifes and abstracts. Before her death on the first day of 1988, she received several honors, including an honorary doctor of fine arts degree from Northwestern State University of Louisiana. Her life and work have inspired biographies, art studies, a documentary, and an opera. Her art hangs in several prestigious museums, including a large collection at the Smithsonian's National Museum of African American History and Culture.

Hunter was born into a Creole family of sharecroppers on the infamous Hidden Hill plantation south of the city of Natchitoches in either late 1886 or early 1887, a mere twenty years after the Civil War ended. Her grandparents had been enslaved. As a young child, Hunter worked in the cotton fields with her father. When she was a teenager, the family moved to Melrose Plantation, also in Natchitoches Parish, for Hunter's father to work as a tenant farmer. Hunter picked cotton and harvested pecans. Starting in the late 1920s, married and with young children, she worked as a housekeeper and a cook for the plantation owners. When Melrose became a salon for creatives in the late 1930s, Hunter painted on found materials with the brushes and paints left behind by visiting artists, though she spoke of having painted long before. She'd created textile works—quilts, woven baskets, tapestries—even earlier. Hunter's husband died in 1944, and to further support her family, she labored all day and painted late into the night. She sold her paintings for pittances, charging a quarter for viewing them in her tiny cabin. A few regional shows in the 1940s and an article in a national magazine in 1953 gave her work wider exposure. In 1955, she became the first African American to have a solo exhibition at the present-day New Orleans Museum of Art, an event she couldn't attend due to Jim Crow laws. By the 1970s, with exhibitions in New York and Los Angeles museums, her work had gained national recognition.

The early 1970s is when my uncle, a White man, intrudes into Hunter's story, taking advantage of the burgeoning market for her art with the creation and sales of his forgeries. At the time of his 1974 arrest, I was twelve years old. I didn't learn of it until he was indicted by a federal grand jury—in 2010. He'd been arrested the previous year for selling even more forgeries of Hunter's art. The news of the indictment showed up on my doorstep.

Subsequently, I searched for more information about his crimes—past and present—in online articles, in museum exhibitions. Reading the statements Uncle Bill gave to journalists, I remembered the background and context for some of his unchallenged and unexplored tales. When the shock of the news dissipated somewhat, I realized I had a story to tell that wasn't being told: a story of family.

Years before my new knowledge about Uncle Bill, I'd tried writing about my mother's family and their New Orleans double-shotgun home. During visits to see my grandparents, I knew my uncle was on the other side of their shared interior wall, though he rarely emerged from his half of the house. I didn't ask questions, but even as a child, I must have sensed mysteries.

With fresh awareness, I opened up the writing I'd set aside and started again, continuing on a journey of discovery, which included the realization that I needed both memoir and fiction to get at the truth, as I know it. To the best of my ability, even in the reimagined third-person sections, I've tried to stay true to the real-life personalities of the main characters—at least true to my memory and to my present-day comprehension. After reading more and more details of Uncle Bill's crimes, I decided there was no point in overly fictionalizing his story. The facts are too sensational on their own.

1

In your life there are a few places, or maybe only the one place, where something happened, and then there are all the other places.
—Alice Munro

WHEN I WAS A CHILD, I pushed out the windows of my uncle's buildings. Decades later, in the nursing home where he was sentenced to live out the remainder of his life, he recalled the incident to my visiting brothers—a family story they'd not heard before, or didn't remember hearing before. I was often told the story and hadn't forgotten it, though whether I remember committing the action is debatable.

When Mama took us to visit her parents, I rarely saw my Uncle Bill, though he and his wife Beryl lived in the other half of my grandparents' double-shotgun house in the Carrollton section of New Orleans, the house Mama grew up in. It was a house with no privacy, which is one reason she loved our house in the suburbs: how different the two homes were.

During our visits, before my grandfather, who worked nights, woke up, Mama and I would sit with my grandmother in the kitchen, the backmost room, at a tiny square table. Though we children called our mother Mama, she called hers Mother; we called our father the same as Mama called hers: Daddy. Those words encapsulated the relationships. The pocket door between the bedroom and the short passageway outside the one bathroom would slide open, and I'd hear Grandpa Toye whistling an Irish tune as he walked through the dining room. He was born in Ireland, and at the time I wondered if Bing Crosby was Irish too. Seeing Crosby on TV Christmas specials every year, I thought he looked like my grandfather, and I connected the two in my mind: fair coloring, a pleasant demeanor, and striking eyes. My own eyes strayed to the words of a plaque on the wall: "Irish Blessing: May the road rise up to meet you." I didn't understand the meaning of that first line, but the rest of the prayer seemed easy enough.

While the adults talked, I stood at Mama's elbow and sketched words with my finger on the red-and-white checkerboard tablecloth. The covering looked as if someone were constantly passing a damp washcloth over it. As soon as Grandpa sat down in the chair I'd vacated, there being only room for three at that table set flush against the wall, Grandma Toye placed in front of him a mug of boiled water and a teabag, its tag and string dangling over the chipped white porcelain. A fishy odor reminded me of the Bucktown seafood store near the levee where Mama shopped for our Friday night dinners. Grandpa Toye picked up the restaurant-style sugar shaker and dumped a considerable amount into his cup, masking the odor and lessening the steam.

My brothers—younger than me, though not by much—would play outside. Before getting up from the table, kneeling on the chair opposite Mama's, I'd watch them from the window. They played between my grandparents' house and the neighbor's, a space I thought was vast; years later I'd realize how narrow it was. The boys ran along the house, brandishing limbs they'd found under the fig tree. If they strayed toward the front, Mama hurried to the side door and yelled at them to stay in the back. The back door, a foot or two away from the kitchen table, was open but screened against mosquitoes, and I saw my brothers become a moving mesh of wire. With no room for me at the table and no interest in playing outside, I'd migrate to the next room.

The dining room's flowered carpet was faded, but each red blossom was distinct among the flat green. I'd point my toes to the center of each rose, imagining myself a ballerina. The side door, also screened, was open to catch the breeze. There was no central air conditioning in the house, unlike in my own. Unless you stood in front of one of the window units in the summer and on other hot days, sweat dripped down your face and arms, and your brain felt sluggish.

I'd once spent the night here. That night the after-bath steam from the clammy bathroom filled the small passageway, meandering into the adjacent dining room on one side and the bedroom on the other. Street noises—cars bumping down potholes, a man's loud then receding laughter—and a streetlamp's bright white light streaming under the slats of the blinds kept me awake. Pressed against the wall, I watched the shadows and became aware of the light rustles of the sleepers: my grandparents and Aunt Helen. The three of them slept in the same room, or so it seemed to me then. Now, after seeing pictures of the rooms on a real-estate site, I know the one bedroom in my memory is two rooms. The sliding doors between them would've been kept open so air could circulate: a shotgun house's *raison d'etre*. As I tried to sleep, I wished with all my little being I was back home. Aunt Helen never forgot how my sleep was disturbed that night, gently teasing me and mentioning it casually in reminiscences for years. I didn't sleep over again.

Sitting on the chair next to the side door, I'd pick up one of Aunt Helen's record albums propped against the console on the floor. Its cover displayed a pensive, almost pouty man with fuzzy blond hair and a funny name: Art Garfunkel. If Aunt Helen had been home and sensed the slightest bit of interest from me, she would've put the record on the player and sung along in a high-pitched, wavery timbre. My brothers' yells soared over the voices murmuring in the kitchen. The boys had drifted to the side of the house again, and I watched them digging in the dirt with their sticks. Grandma's tomato plants were growing, and I hoped no one would see what they were doing. My eyes wandered across a row of paintings. Hung high on picture rails, each painting swung from a hook, the backing strings visible. Some were full-length portraits; none were of anyone I recognized. Some had a religious theme, none were cheerful, and I would've been afraid of them if it had been nighttime. Both Aunt Helen and Uncle Bill painted, but at the time I wasn't aware that he did. I assumed these paintings on this side of the house were my aunt's, and I still believe that to be true.

Writing was another of Aunt Helen's talents, mostly poetry. Her heavy black typewriter sat on a corner of the seemingly massive dining-room table, and I'd sit on her chair, my fingers over the keys, and pretend I knew how to type. I had nothing to say, so I produced a string of nonsense onto the paper inside the roller. On a TV tray, shoved even farther into the recess, were books and papers threatening to spill to the floor; they didn't, nor did the piles of reading materials in the front room. The stuffy smell was worse there than anywhere else in the house—perhaps because the front door was never opened, always locked as far as I knew, the chain perpetually looped through the deadbolt.

Sometimes I'd wander to the front of the house after Grandpa was awake, through the dining room, past the bathroom with its pale-pink sink and tub, past the bedroom(s), and into the front room. Sitting in an old sunken armchair, I'd flip through whatever book was on top of the tower of books, newspapers, and magazines next to the chair. Unnested wooden Russian dolls were lined up in a row on top of the low bookcase under the window. At the time, I thought Aunt Helen had visited the Soviet Union, but I wasn't sure. Her many stories confused me, and I was never sure which were true or what they meant. My nose twitched, and I sneezed at the dust. I read sentences here and there from the book on my lap, hardly understanding any of them, but luxuriating in the shapes and supposed sounds of the words. Much later I'd discover that many of the words didn't sound the way they looked and, in my head, I'd been saying them wrong.

BACK in the dining room, I heard the lovely British-accented voice of Aunt Beryl wafting over to my side-door perch. I never saw her arrive, only knew that she had. The screen door at the back of the house hadn't creaked. The lock on the front door hadn't turned. No communicating door between the two halves of the house existed, but at Beryl's appearance I'd imagine there must be one, wondering why I couldn't find the secret door that swung out from one of the unused fireplaces. Still holding the album, I leaned to the right and caught a glimpse of Aunt Beryl standing in the kitchen. She was explaining to Mama why Uncle Bill couldn't come over to say hello: He wasn't feeling well. He rarely felt well. I thought Beryl pretty; her hair was dark, and her clothes seemed too nice for a next-door visit. Mama never went to the other side of the house, but Beryl always knew when we were at my grandparents'. Perhaps she heard us through the shared wall—the extra voice in the kitchen, one of my brother's rapid footsteps as he rushed inside to use the bathroom, clanking the toilet seat, running out again. Uncle Bill and I seemed to be the only silent beings.

I wondered what my uncle was doing, but I didn't mind not seeing him. I was a little bit afraid of him, but then I was a little bit afraid of almost everyone. Now, I wonder if my uncle was painting one of his forgeries and had no time to visit, or if he was suffering one of his mental-breakdown episodes and was in bed—catatonic or curled up in a fetal position. Only Beryl would know. Years later I was told about his shock treatments and that he was agoraphobic. Even later, I was told he was difficult to deal with. He'd ask family members for favors, then berate them when they didn't arrive quickly enough or they didn't want to spend any more of their money on a failing venture. But there was much we were not told.

I RECALL my dad, sitting in his chair in the family den, slightly shaking his head, making a cryptic comment about Uncle Bill's brilliance and if only he'd used it for good. You didn't question Daddy's pronouncements; you'd get no further information. It was as if he were talking to himself. I recall this comment decades later—February 2010, four years after my father's death—when I first read about the indicted Baton Rouge art forger William Toye. The article in the local newspaper mentions his having been arrested in April 1974, also for forgery. A piece of an old forgotten puzzle slides into place, as I immediately realize this earlier arrest was what Daddy had been referring to. For thirty-six years, our parents had kept this information from us, not mentioning it once in my presence.

By 1974, Mama must've been going to see her parents while we were in school, because our visits seem to have decreased; or maybe I was allowed to stay home while my youngest siblings were taken along. My brother Kevin, two years younger than me, remembers being packed in the car after a visit—our mother saying she needed to go back to the house for some reason—and only then speaking with Uncle Bill on his side of the front porch, as if she didn't want us to hear a word he said. I don't remember this. If I was there, I might've had my mind and eyes on a book; I carried one everywhere.

During one visit to my grandparents, Mama and I walked the few blocks to Nix Library. We crossed the tree-lined Carrollton Avenue with the streetcar track going down its middle to a big red-brick building. Visiting this library as an adult, I realize it's not big; Nix is almost as narrow as the double-shotgun house I once thought wide. In front of the low shelving, Mama muttered that Grandpa was running out of books to read. I looked at the other shelves and couldn't imagine such a thing. At work, as a security guard for an apartment building, he read all night and he'd almost finished the mysteries the branch offered. Mama ended up ordering him a subscription to *Ellery Queen's Mystery Magazine*, but she had it mailed to our house, and I read the issues before she got around to bringing them to him. I gorged on their stories as I did any new reading material I found.

While Mama and I went to the library, my siblings were with Grandma Toye picking figs. Walking back with a pile of books in my arms, I thought of the pastel-green plastic bowl Grandma used for fig-picking and how it'd be waiting, full, on her white kitchen counter next to the sink. We'd be sent home with some figs and, standing at our pale-pink kitchen counter, Mama would peel each one with a knife and pop the naked meat into our waiting mouths as if we were baby birds. I marveled that not a trace of flesh was left attached to the skin when she was done. My grandparents lived on Plum Street, but in my head I always had to make the adjustment from thinking of it as Fig Street.

Off to the side from the fig tree, set against a weathered wooden fence at the back edge of the property, was a long shed, a workroom Uncle Bill had built for himself. As an older child, I once followed my brothers inside after they'd pushed open its rusty door. We flipped a light switch, but nothing happened. I stepped over the rotting threshold, almost tripping over a fallen beam. Sunlight from the open door was the only illumination. Making our way inside, despite the dimness, we could see the shed was full of junk, or so it seemed to us. A worktable against the back wall held architectural models Bill had designed and built; lined against a side wall were canvases in various stages of creation. When we pressed upon the squeezed tubes of paint, nothing emerged. The wooden surface the tubes sat upon was marked by colors, dried-up blobs of yellow and red and blue. Like the inhabitants of Sleeping Beauty's castle, all was as if frozen in time, except for the dust motes moving within the humid breath of air from the open doorway. Based on the look of his workroom, I didn't think Uncle Bill used it any longer. As my brothers continued to explore, looking for whatever they could find to take away for their backyard games, I carefully retraced my steps, my only interest in the shed being the setting of the story I'd heard since I was much younger.

In that family story, Uncle Bill sat me on his lap at the table in his shed in front of his model buildings. His name for me was Baby Doll. I was small for my age, and until I was about four years old, my dark hair fell in corkscrew ringlets down the sides of my face. Before my first day of kindergarten, Mama chopped off my curls, hoping to combat the messy tangles we both cried over as she tried to brush them out. The nickname confused me: my baby dolls had blue eyes, blonde hair, and creamy white skin; I looked nothing like them. I doubt I realized it at the time, but the windows and doors of the balsa-wood buildings had been outlined with a blade. Uncle Bill instructed me to poke at the soon-to-be openings with my finger. As I did so, knowing my brothers were too young for such an important task, I felt powerful, special—or I imagine I felt that way, since it's how I felt when I heard the story repeated.

I could use this punching out of windows and doors as a symbol of destruction. Or I could offer it as a metaphor for letting in air and light to an enclosed structure, one that my mother tried to keep that way.

2

*It was really the world that was one's brutal mother, the one that nursed and
neglected you, and your own mother was only your sibling in that world.*
                                                          —Lorrie Moore

THE NEWSPAPER of February 26, 2010, was laid out in front of me,
spread across the kitchen counter—black-and-white across a sea of
blue—a steaming pot of tea under the soft cozy I'd treated myself to after
my mother had left my home. After suffering a stroke, she'd lived with
my husband Tom and me for nine months and had recently returned to
her own home after a brief time in an assisted-living residence. While
she was here, I hated being pulled so abruptly into the mornings, already
exhausted before the day began. Now the mornings were my favorite
time of day—the house empty, no one demanding my time. I eased into
the rest of the day with tea and toast, sipping between each slow bite.

I tried not to think of the days past. I joked with friends and family
that I had PTSD from caring for my mother, though maybe it wasn't a
joke. Back then I'd had a dream of using a block of white chalk to smooth
myself out, length by length, from my head to my toes in three consecu-
tive draws down and up. It wouldn't have helped. The left side of my neck
still hurt, as did the right side of my jaw. Battle wounds: a degenerative
disc in my neck yanked when my mom had panicked as I was moving
her from bed to wheelchair; and bruxism from the tension of knowing
that the beep of the walkie-talkie—her way of calling for help during the
night—could wake me at any time.

I started with the Living section, carefully tearing out the crossword
puzzle for Tom; then I read the Sports, noting what games we'd watch
that night. I'd lost the habit of reading the Comics when there was no
time for such frivolities. I flipped back to the front section. I turned to
page 2, scanning the headlines. Below the fold, the words "art forger"
caught my eye and I looked at the brief article with interest. My heart

jumped when I saw the name: *William J. Toye*. Okay, I told myself in the pause of a heartbeat, maybe there's more than one man by that name—even in the state of Louisiana, even in the city of Baton Rouge, though I didn't believe it. Then my eye landed on the name of the man's wife, also indicted, along with an art dealer named Robert Lucky, whose name I didn't recognize. Perhaps there was more than one William Toye in the area, but certainly only one with a wife named Beryl.

The last thing I felt like doing was calling my mom to tell her. Her stroke the year before had left her confined to a wheelchair, though she was able to use the right side of her body. I told myself she needed to be told the news gently, and in person, but that wasn't the real reason I didn't call her. The stroke hadn't taken away her mental faculties; she'd kept tight control of everything she wanted to since she'd moved into my home after being discharged from the hospital in March of 2009.

I knew that Ted, the brother closest to me in age, would be taking her to a doctor's appointment later that day, so I called him, told him about the article, and asked him to tell her in person, feeling guilty about leaving another task to him. As when she lived with me, he visited her almost every day—overseeing her exercises, dropping off the shopping he did for her.

Much later that day, later than I thought it would be, she called me. "He's living in Baton Rouge. Why would they write about it in the New Orleans paper?" The naiveté—or, more accurately, self-delusion—shouldn't have astounded me, but it did. As with other events throughout her life, she'd convinced herself this too was tucked away where no one she knew could find it. I was also astounded that she wasn't astounded by the news. It wasn't news to her.

One phone call was never sufficient for my mom to complete a conversation. She'd hang up and almost immediately call back with a detail, one she'd been leading to but avoiding the first time. This time it was to say an FBI agent had come to her house shortly after she'd returned to it. She had no information for the agent; she hadn't talked to her older brother in years. I can see her rolling her wheelchair to the front door, ascertaining who was behind it, then turning the two locks, one with a key she kept in a drawer of the low end-table near the door. I imagine my mother and the agent, with mutual sympathy, talking about the 1974 arrest: the one never prosecuted, the one I learned of from the article that morning.

My brothers and I scoured the internet and emailed links to one another, surprised by what had been kept from us. The FBI raided Bill and Beryl's Baton Rouge home in September of 2009. My mother had lived with me in the New Orleans area from mid-March through early December 2009. She'd receive calls on her cell phone, but I'd give her privacy, leaving the room she was in when one came through. We had innumerable conversations about all kinds of things during this time, but she said nothing about her brother Bill's crimes. Had the secret become so entrenched that the telling of it had become too difficult? How could she begin? How to say the first word? It was likely easier for her to believe the news of his arrest wouldn't make its way to New Orleans.

Ted thought to check Wikipedia, and there was an entry, scant of details; more would be added in time. In several months I would see one of Aunt Helen's best friends at a 2011 poetry event for another of her best friends, and the first thing the former would say to me is, "They told Bill not to do it again. How could he!" I would nod, knowing what she's referring to and imagining my bafflement if I hadn't seen the article the year before.

I'd felt shock, a state that lasted for weeks. A low-grade headache became my constant companion. My new knowledge teemed beneath the surface of my mind as I slept. As a coping tactic, I told myself it was not as if Uncle Bill had committed murder. It felt that way; it felt as if he'd killed, or at least stolen, a part of Clementine Hunter's life.

Dark humor took over, shared only with my husband and brothers. I became annoyed that the writers of the feature articles about Bill had not sought out his relatives, as far as I could tell, for their memories or opinions. The implication seemed to be my uncle had no relatives—at least none that mattered—excepting two: his accomplice-wife and the alcoholic father Bill blamed for shaping the outcome of his life. The other implication seemed to be that Bill's delusions of grandeur were plucked from the air. As I read the articles, I remembered the factual bases to some of his outlandish claims.

I know some family stories, but there's much I don't know, especially because of my mother's reticence about Bill's shameful activities. Even if she'd been forthcoming, family stories contain mistakes, self-delusions, lies—even if the lies aren't willful. A family member repeats an oft-told story of an event where she wasn't present and in the latest iteration places herself there with other details changed. Not wanting to be rude, I don't correct her; but by my not doing so, is the story permanently twisted out of shape? Will her son, whom the story is about, repeat wrong details to a future generation one day? If I correct these details now, is it too late? Have the mistakes already hardened?

When I view the real-estate photos of the interior of the Plum Street house, I'm surprised at how small the rooms are, especially the bedrooms. Already my memories seem fraudulent, yet they are true to the child I was. Memory is unreliable; it might as well be fiction.

3

A Starter House

At the front of the house Billy drew in the dirt with a stick. He saw the building before it appeared under his hand. It was bigger than the house he lived in, almost as big as the church they attended, with a prepossessing, though cross-less, roof. He had no interest in its interior. He took for granted that would be his mother's domain or perhaps his sister's when she grew up. Right now she was a mewling baby, and he had no interest in her either.

As he widened the dimensions, the stick was pulled from his hand; a shadow loomed over him and his house. "What you doing, son?" The voice was slurred, and Billy cringed. He knew what that meant. "Ah— you're drawing. That's a good one too. You are good at the drawings." His father was in a crouch, and as he tried to stand, he fell, obliterating the majority of Billy's house with his flailing arms and kicking Billy in the shin with his work boot. Billy wasn't sure which hurt more. Tears stung his eyes, and he backed away.

Mother appeared at the front door with the baby on her shoulder, then disappeared. When she returned, Kay wasn't with her, though Billy heard her wailing through the screen door. Mother ran to the other side of the house to Aunt Ethel's, and when she returned with Uncle Dick, Daddy was snoring.

"Ah, the boy," Uncle Dick crooned. "That's a nasty bruise you're going to have." The sympathy Billy craved was enough to tip the tears down his lower eyelids. Uncle Dick hoisted his brother. They were both thin, angular men, but at present one of them was a deadweight.

As Uncle Dick carry-dragged Daddy into their side of the house, Billy pulled himself up. His stick, the one he'd hidden under the stoop because it was perfect for drawing, was broken. Billy huffed: No more tears, he told himself. He squinted in the waning sunlight that bounced off the silver branches of the tree. Shifting into the shade, moving out of sight of Mother who might be standing at the door, he snapped off a low-hanging branch. It was as smooth as skin. He bent down to draw the leaves he saw above his head, but having no color to them, his looked dead. He ran back to the drawing of his house.

With a critical eye, he repaired what Daddy had smashed. He winced as his shin touched the ground. The red swollen welt held his interest for only a moment, and he added galleries and cornices until the sun went down and Mother called him in to dinner. He hadn't noticed Uncle Dick leaving their side of the house or heard his goodbye as he did.

He brushed off his knees and left his shoes on the stoop. He heard Mother in the kitchen and didn't need to be told to wash his hands. Mother had set the radio to the classical music station, and the sounds were soothing. When Daddy ate with them, the radio was turned to an incomprehensible ball game. Near the radio sat Mother's sewing machine, fabric folded neatly next to it. Billy used to shift her spools of thread around—comparing the yellows to the greens, the greens to the blues—until she'd asked him to stop reorganizing her system.

He sat on a kitchen chair and bit into the thick sandwich: bread Mother had baked the day before, salted leftover chicken inside. She'd killed the chicken herself, and he'd watched its body run around the yard as its head lay on the ground. He barely tasted the morsel in his mouth as he set the beige sandwich on the bright-white plate to sketch with his finger on the red-and-white tablecloth. He needed colors! "I need colors, Mother," he said.

"Your box of crayons is in the chifforobe."

"Those aren't good enough." He shook his head, sadly and respectfully. "May I have some paints, like the ones Liebermann must've used?" He'd stared for hours at the print of a flower garden that used to hang in the front room. Despite Mother's explanations, he didn't understand why it was no longer there. Without trying, he could still see it.

"You mustn't speak of him, especially not at school. Do you under-stand?" She stood up from the table and moved her plate to the sink. "After Mrs. Zeller picks up her skirt, I'll buy you some of those colored pencils I've seen. Now finish eating. It's almost bedtime." A crying sound escalated as Mother left the kitchen.

The Liebermann print, a wedding gift from one of Mother's relatives, was taken down when she'd explained she was no longer German. Mother said if anyone asked, she was descended from the Irish, with a little bit of Scots thrown in, like Daddy. When Billy got his colors, he'd draw the painting from memory and not add the man's name to it.

He bathed, then read at the table Mother had cleared and wiped. She'd pulled the blinds against the outside darkness, and a bare bulb lit up the room. He'd read all the books they owned and was reading the newspaper. On Sundays there was only one, but it was big enough to extend throughout the day. He couldn't fall asleep if he hadn't read something new first. The art books he'd committed to memory belonged to the public library.

In his small bed under the window, Billy drifted toward sleep—until the voices commenced. He turned toward the wall. Through the slats of the blinds, a streetlight blazed. He was forced to listen to the voices' conversations. Most of it was nonsense, like Daddy's baseball games.

4

M Y FATHER, who didn't say things lightly, called his brother-in-law a genius. I imagine both Bill's genius and mental illness started early.

Kay is my mother. She was named Mary Katherine after her two grandmothers but was called Kay from the time of her birth. My grandmother's maiden name was Hinrichs; I've seen it also spelled Heinrichs. My mother didn't talk of their German ancestry because her mother didn't; I came to believe that was due to World War II, when German families were denying their roots.

My grandparents were married on August 13, 1930, when Grandpa was thirty-four and Grandma twenty-five. Bill was born August 15, 1931. Before the Plum Street house, my grandparents' residence, including at the time of my mother's birth in 1938, was on Cambronne Street, at the corner of Plum. The Cambronne address is listed on my grandfather's naturalization papers when my mom would've been four or five. Though I don't remember her mentioning the Cambronne home, it was likely formative for Bill. Listed on real-estate sites as being a multifamily home built in 1920, the Cambronne house sits squat and long, claustrophobically close to another house on one side, open to Plum Street on the other. Grandpa's parents lived on Willow Street, around the corner from the Plum Street home.

My grandmother's sister, Ethel, married my grandfather's brother, Richard. They and their two children lived for a while in the other half of the Plum Street house, the half that Bill and Beryl would eventually take over. Photos of the sisters from before their marriages show the girls in matching dresses, my smiling grandmother with her arm draped over Ethel's shoulders. I imagine the closeness of the two sisters and the two brothers: dating, marrying, and buying the Plum Street house together for their growing families. I don't remember my great-aunt and great-uncle living in the Plum Street home; at some point they moved, selling their portion to my grandparents.

5

A Shotgun House

"BE STILL," Billy commanded. "No fidgeting." Kay wore a painted cardboard crown and Billy was sketching her. In an effort to please, her face held a serious expression. Their younger sister Helen had the imperious look he wanted, even at four years old, but he'd given up trying to coerce her into sitting still. He was proud of the crown he'd made for the Carnival celebration at school. Created from the backing boards he'd hoarded from Daddy's shirts, it had won a school prize. Though the crown looked more real than not, the blanket he'd draped over Kay's shoulders for a royal stole didn't look real at all. He'd change it for the painting: Reality was not his goal.

"You may leave now, your Royal Highness."

Kay giggled and ran out the side door to the front of the house. Billy knew their cousin Pat was on her side of the porch waiting patiently for Kay. Old enough to understand what double-cousins meant, the two girls were thrilled at the fact, and Billy was tired of hearing them talk about it.

Daddy appeared in the kitchen as Billy was filling his rinse cup at the sink. "That's a fine drawing. You've captured Kay well."

"Thank you." Billy's words were clipped. He was never in the mood to be polite to Daddy after one of his drunken episodes. Coffee sloshed on the counter as Daddy poured some into a mug, and Billy felt no sympathy upon seeing the man's shaky hands and facial pallor. A tea-drinking man, Daddy only drank coffee after a binge.

The one time Billy recalled being proud of Daddy was when he became an American citizen. The U.S. had been at war for six months, and it was a relief to the family that Daddy was not German, or even Italian. Daddy commented that his being listed in the newspaper as being from Great Britain rankled, but they knew he was too giddy not to be joking. The ceremony was two days before the conclusion of Midway; there was much to celebrate that weekend. And celebrate Daddy did, ruining it all.

Billy sat in front of the easel in the dining room as the girls ran in. Kay spotted their father and ran toward him. She seemed to have a knack for knowing when he was awake. "Daddy!" She threw her arms around him, and Billy turned away in disgust.

"Ah, my little colleen," Daddy crooned. "And here's bonny Pat." He put his other arm around his niece to envelop her in their hug.

Kay giggled. "You know my name's not Colleen."

"And you," Daddy said, as he touched the tip of Kay's nose, "know *colleen* means 'girl.'"

All of this was a routine, and Billy did his best to ignore it.

Daddy extricated himself from the arms of the girls and sat at the tiny kitchen table with its red-and-white oilcloth. He poured an excessive amount of sugar into his mug and stirred his coffee as he murmured the words to "When Irish Eyes Are Smiling."

Kay looked at him with shining eyes. "I love those Irish songs you sing."

"That isn't an Irish song. It's American."

"You sing the word 'Irish.'"

Daddy chuckled. "Even so."

The magic of his painting broken, Billy slouched into his parents' bedroom and approached the crib slowly, his feet hushed on the wooden floor. His lanky fingers touched the baby's smooth bare leg in a silent communion, and in a reflexive motion Philip turned toward him. Not for the first time, Billy wondered if one of the voices he heard at night belonged to Philip. That one voice whispered loving words only he could understand.

Unlike when the girls were babies, Philip didn't cry. His legs were immobile, and he'd hardly grown since he was born. Mother blamed the doctor, who'd panicked when the birth happened too quickly for her. Billy wasn't clear on the details—Mother would never speak of intimate matters in front of her son—but he'd overheard her telling Aunt Ethel she was done with female doctors.

6

M Y MOTHER and her cousin Pat were proud of being double-cousins: Closer than sisters, they'd say. Mama seemed to always get along with her sister Helen, but she had more in common with Pat, who had a brother. When I was a child, Pat and her two children would visit us when they were in town to see other relatives. Over a simple lunch of ham po-boys and potato chips at the big kitchen table, Mama and Pat would tell us kids, once again, about their double-cousin status. I wasn't clear if that relationship descended to us second cousins. Seeing one another rarely, we were awkward at first, a stark contrast to the relationships my siblings and I had with our first cousins on Daddy's side. Near the end of Pat's life, during her last visit to New Orleans, she and I sat on my mom's sofa, Mama next to us in her wheelchair, and they told me the double-cousin story one last time as we looked at photos of their grandchildren.

Pat's brother was called Dickie to distinguish him from their father, Richard. Of course, he was a double-cousin to my mom and her siblings too, but I never heard the term used in any relationship except my mother and Pat's. In a photo dated 1940, when Billy was eight or nine and Dickie four or five, the two boys sit on a house stoop. They look younger than their purported ages. Billy has dirty knees and a stubborn expression; Dickie looks to the side, smiling sweetly.

The date on my grandfather's naturalization papers is June 4, 1942. I know nothing else of the event. My mother was open with us about his being her favorite parent; she made it sound inevitable: "How could he not be?" She chuckled over his explaining to her that "When Irish Eyes Are Smiling" is an American song. Grandpa Toye hummed it many times as we sat in that tiny kitchen on Plum Street. At the end of the funeral Mass held for my mom, the Irish priest, without any prompting from us, the family, led the congregation in the singing of that American song.

I have one photograph of my mother's brother Philip. On its back, in neat handwriting, likely my grandmother's, is written "Picture taken Aug

30. 1944." Next to that, written in pencil, is "Born 4-18-1944," which I recognize as Mama's handwriting. His birth-registration card confirms the date. The boy in the crib, its bars visible on either side, looks long for a four-month-old, but height ran in the family, so that doesn't seem unusual. Nothing in his face or limbs suggests there's anything wrong with him. According to the story my mom told, as my grandmother was rolled down the hospital hallway, Philip's head began to emerge. The doctor, who was a woman, panicked and closed my grandmother's legs together, likely depriving Philip of oxygen. Forceps were used in the delivery room. My grandmother refused to go to another female doctor.

7

A Heartbroken Home

"Kay." Mother's sharp voice broke into the dining room. "Come here now. I need you to hold Wayne." Kay, more than willing, ran into the bedroom. She returned with the baby, and she and Helen set him between them on the floor, cooing baby talk to Wayne, who became increasingly excited and huffy, as if he was trying to talk back. The girls were delighted.

"William." Mother's voice was even louder this time. Billy knew Daddy was the William she wanted, so he stayed in front of his easel, preparing his paints. Daddy got up quicker than Billy would've ever expected, knocking over the chair—the newspaper he'd been reading drifting to the floor. His voice was heard from the bedroom. "Billy, call Dick at work and ask him to come get us. Philip's in distress." No one thought to call the new emergency medical transport. Their response time was not good—at least a half hour no matter where you lived, not counting the time it would take to get to the hospital.

Billy ran to the phone on the kitchen wall, his fingers trembling as he dialed—their length seeming longer than usual, even crooked in his haste. Kay stood in the doorway, Wayne in her arms, her eyes big and scared. "Bring Wayne to Aunt Ethel's. Now. Tell her something's wrong with Philip." The always-obedient Kay was gone from his sight immediately, Helen at her heels.

After hanging up the phone, Billy tried to move toward the bedroom. His hands were still shaking, and he was having trouble breathing. The room spun and he grabbed the back of a dining chair. "Billy, what is it? You're white as a haunt. I thought something was wrong with Philip." Aunt Ethel shoved him in the chair and put his head between his knees. The sound of crying took her away from him. He knew it was too late to say goodbye.

MOTHER put Wayne in his crib, next to the empty one. Next to Helen, Kay hiccupped herself to sleep. There being no point in going to the hospital, Uncle Dick had walked to the corner to get the priest and escorted him back after he was finished with his ministrations. Aunt Ethel hugged Billy before she left. He sat with his parents in the dining room—no one speaking, their eyes not meeting, Daddy crying. Abruptly Daddy got up and grabbed his hat from the top of the chifforobe. "William," Mother said, one quick word doing no good. He was gone. Billy went to bed, knowing Mother would need him to help Daddy into bed when he returned in the small hours.

Billy's sleep was unexpectedly untroubled, and when he woke, he wondered if the voices had fled along with his brother.

8

MY MOTHER never said anything about Philip's death, only that they knew he wouldn't live long. She was six when he was born; Bill was almost thirteen. I don't know if Philip's life and death held meaning for Bill, but I became fond of the metaphor of a closeness between the two brothers—both damaged, though in different ways.

I don't know when Philip died; I think Mama said he was about five, maybe as old as seven. Due to his health issues from birth, I believe he never left a crib, though my memory of that could be wrong or the story I was told exaggerated. I didn't find an obituary; perhaps there wasn't one. A scrapbook from Bill's teenage years starts with newspaper clippings about school politics: an embattled high-school civics teacher, supported by students, cleared by the school board for not stressing "Americanism" in her classes. Pasted on a later page is a cartoon that "young Bill" drew for a contest sponsored by a local shoppers' guide. Titled "No Place to Play," it depicts a traffic jam alongside a streetcar. Bill is described as "of slight build and not able to go in for football and the like because of his health, at least for the present, does aspire to be an artist." I'm struck by the casual stereotyping, and I imagine Bill being bullied, his insecurity, and the need to justify his interest in art and not sports. The piece ends with saying "Mrs. Toye" is "rearing five children, the youngest being a little boy of seven months." Since the fifth child, Wayne, was born in February of 1947, this undated article has to be from around September of the same year. Bill is stated as being fifteen; Philip would've been three.

Philip is not mentioned in either of my grandparents' obituaries, or in either of his sisters'. I have a vague memory of briefly wondering if I should include him in my mother's obituary, but I didn't remember him in my aunt's, and my mother had written hers. It was a trying time and it seemed one more thing to deal with, so I didn't.

During my research, I had trouble finding Grandpa Toye's obituary because it's listed under Jay Toye. As far as I know, he was never known by Jay, or by his middle name Joseph, or even by the initial of his middle name. Memory and newspapers get things wrong, but this mistake seems odd, even taking into consideration that immigrants' names are in flux when they arrive at their destination. My father implied his family was lucky to have been able to keep both *m*'s in their surname of Tumminello after going through immigration. Grandpa Toye's birth certificate lists his middle name as Stanislaus; on his naturalization papers it's Joseph. His father's first name is listed as John on my grandfather's (Irish) birth certificate, and it's Sean on my grandfather's (U.S.) death certificate: It seems to me it should be the other way around.

At my mother's funeral, Uncle Wayne told me Philip is his guardian angel. His wife concurred. I was both surprised and pleased to know that Philip was remembered in such a way. Wayne would've been a toddler when Philip died, perhaps with no clear memories of the trauma his life and death caused the rest of the family. But if Wayne had been the one to write the obituaries of family members, maybe he would've included Philip.

9

An Opera House

THE SCHOOL'S PIGEON-GRAY WALLS moved inward, closer and closer. Billy tried to quicken his pace, but his legs wouldn't cooperate. He tried to shrink into himself, but he was already as thin as a blade. He scuttled sideways like a crab, and his panic turned him as red as one that'd been boiled, laid out on newspaper, ready to be picked apart and eaten. Bumped on both sides, he collapsed, his knees folding like the Hotch Potch character that taught colonial children their ABCs. Scrunched into a ball, resembling no letter from any alphabet, he went blank.

KAY watched as Billy was brought through the open side door. It was different than when Daddy stumbled in, needing help. Daddy's eyes would be as glazed as Billy's were now, but Billy was weak and Daddy was not. Mother and Billy would support Daddy, one on either side, and he'd be belting out a tune at the top of his lungs and fighting them both. Mother would bite out harsh words to quiet him, and Kay wondered why she bothered; they never worked. Billy would remain as silent as he was now, his face sad. Now it held a vacant expression, and Kay was the one who was sad.

She knew Billy was at his best when busy, but his frantic activity turned into a sleepless frenzy, which led to his treatments. During these periods he didn't sleep, didn't stop talking, and kept everyone awake with his pacing from the front room to the dining room. He'd bring in his opera-set models from the shed. He'd pore over his books and tinker with his models all day and all night, obsessing over the details. The evidence sat on the dining table.

BILLY didn't remember. He didn't remember what led to his hospitalization. He didn't remember the details of his stay there. His body remembered. After being carried inside—Daddy on one side, Uncle Dick on

27

the other—he was led to the bed and slept the sleep of the dead, except for the times his body seemed to jolt upwards. When he woke, Kay was in front of him—recently awake herself, he surmised—her hair matted to one side of her head, the other side a wiry mess. Her eyes looked sad, their hazel depths like the shadow under the pool table in van Gogh's *The Night Cafe*. It was almost the first color he noticed; the edges of his awareness were still a dim gray.

"Mother," he heard her say as she left the room, "I think Billy's awake," and he drifted back into sleep.

MOTHER pulled out a dining-table chair, and as Billy sat down he tried to focus on what she was saying. It dawned on him she was making plans. "No," he sputtered. "I'm not going back to school."

"That's what I'm saying, Billy. Your father and I have decided you can attend De La Salle." An image of the cool white building appeared before his eyes: The leafy green oaks shading it were inviting, then the streetcar came clanking down the avenue. It used to be what he wanted, the all-boys Catholic school whose tuition would be difficult for his parents to pay.

"I mean I'm not going to any school." His fingers curled around the edge of the table. "I'm sixteen. I'm done."

Mother was silent. Billy knew she was stunned. "Kay," she finally said, "you're done with your dinner; please check on Wayne. Then tell Helen to hurry with her bath so you can take yours." Kay scrambled down from the chair, and Mother waited until she heard Kay's footsteps leave the passageway. "What do you mean by this? You're brilliant. You need your education."

"My grades are poor. There's nothing they can teach me." His eyes wandered to his easel in the corner. "I'll get a job."

"Doing what?" Mother's eyes were sharp through her spiky glasses. She's all points and angles, he thought; he understood he was too. "I'll not have you be a laborer like your father. What a waste it's been for him—and would be for you."

"Daddy was a machinist. He had a skill." He thought of the blueprints his father scanned and understood in a flash. Daddy could've been more, could've stayed where he was, maybe even advanced, before drink got in the way. "But I have no intention of ever being like Daddy, and I will find work."

He put his fork down. He'd eaten hardly anything, the sight of the congealing butter in the mashed potatoes a wasted pool of yellow, the same color behind van Gogh's sunflowers. He thought of Kay wanting the stray sunflower in the vegetable garden, crying when she couldn't pull it up, falling on her bottom with the effort. Mother had fussed at her to be quiet, saying sunflowers were not meant to be picked. Why not, he thought? Van Gogh must've picked some, set them in a vase to paint them. He gazed at his easel. Tomorrow, if he had the strength, he'd paint van Gogh's flowers for Kay.

BILLY took the streetcar downtown and walked the few blocks toward his new summer classes, a compromise between him and Mother. At the sight of the ten-year-old Art Deco edifice, he stopped to analyze it. The molding alongside the striking glass door and the figures above it were Greek-influenced, the school's name—L. E. Rabouin Memorial— inscribed in an Egyptian style. His eye flowed back to the door, to the sideways-T-shaped glass panes thrusting into smaller squared ones.

He shook off his reverie and pulled on the heavy door. The coolness inside was a balm. Down the main hallway, he passed administration offices and, off an artery, found the room, its door propped open, words on a standing sign proclaiming the tailoring class.

The instructor asked for introductions. Two women, friends, looking much like Mother and Aunt Ethel, said they wanted to learn something new, thought they'd like this kind of work. A Marine veteran gave his name. The teacher didn't press for more; if she had, Billy would've expected Mr. Marine to bark out only his name again, maybe adding rank and serial number. During his turn, Billy waxed almost poetic on his reasons for taking the class. He said he planned on having a tailoring firm someday and, after the summer course was over, he'd study design and fashion at the New Orleans Academy of Art. The women, certainly aware of the academy's selective admission standards, cooed appreciatively. Billy didn't mention his mother's background as a home seamstress or that she'd forced him to take the tailoring class. If he wasn't completing high school, she said, he had to do something.

THE STRAINS of the "Triumphal March" from the opera *Aida* filled the house as Bill, carrying a broom, pretended to be a spear-carrying Egyptian soldier. He'd positioned Kay and Pat next to each other, instructing them to pretend Mother was behind them with her hands on their shoulders.

Helen came running in. "I want to play."

Bill lowered the volume. "Quiet. We are not playing. We're rehearsing the grand return of a victorious army."

"I'm rehearsing too." Arms akimbo, she looked him in the eyes, daring him to contradict her.

Bill scowled. "Mother, would you please tell Helen to leave us alone? This is important. I want Kay and Pat to be familiar with their scene before dress rehearsals."

Mother stopped on her way through the dining room with a basket of dry laundry, plucked from the clothesline, on her hip. "Don't raise your voice; Wayne's napping. Helen, either come help me or listen to Bill." At eighteen he'd convinced his family to stop using the diminutive of his name, at least most of the time. His work on the production of an opera, including its set design, should've gained him some respect.

He knew Helen wouldn't go away, so he positioned her in front of the older girls and told her to stay put. He picked up the tonearm of the record player and started the song over. At the back-and-forth melody, Helen swayed her head, hips, and arms. Kay and Pat giggled. He stopped the music. "Helen, you must be serious." She nodded, her lips pressed together firmly. He placed the needle back on the record, and the music swelled again.

The older girls collapsed into giggles, and he looked behind him. Helen was attempting a headstand, her legs flailing with the struggle. "Never mind—we'll try later," said Bill. He went sulking to his corner of the room, picked up a paintbrush, and flicked off imaginary dust from his canvas.

"Kay," Helen called out, her head between her legs, "teach me how to stand on my head."

Kay glanced at her brother. "We need the back of the armchair. Come on." The three girls headed toward the front room—Kay leading, Helen skipping behind.

KAY glided her finger across one of Bill's *Aida* models, from the top of a column to a ripple in the drapery. She jumped as footsteps sounded on the wooden floor of the passageway. They were muffled by the carpet as Bill entered the dining room. "Ready?" he asked, tugging on his tie. She reluctantly left the small, detailed building at the corner of the table and followed Bill out the door. Wayne was with the next-door neighbor. Helen was with Aunt Ethel and Uncle Dick. They would come to the auditorium later; Bill had left their tickets to the opera at the door.

He'd told Mother he could handle Kay and Pat by himself. He'd assured her they'd get to the supernumeraries' green room safe and sound, but she insisted: She was coming along and would brook no more discussion. He knew not to bring it up again. She'd made the white robes for the children, and her presence would be useful if any last-minute adjustments were needed. No one should say she didn't belong backstage.

The four of them walked the two blocks to the streetcar line. There was no hint of autumn in the mid-October air, though it no longer felt like triple digits. They stood under the shade of an oak tree until the car clanged up the line, making its turn from the grander street around the bend.

Bill settled into a seat and thought of his set models. They'd been reproduced in striking detail. It was a marvel to see them appear in rehearsals: huge pillars incised with carvings of flat human figures and palm branches; the two huge statues of royalty; the feline stone images of the gods. He'd brought a stray into the house to sketch it, and after feeding it tuna from a can and milk from the refrigerator, it had stayed.

He heard the girls' chatter. When they got to the auditorium, he knew that would cease. Kay was painfully shy; she looked down and away when she encountered unfamiliar people, hoping they wouldn't notice her. He understood that feeling, though he mostly craved attention—especially from strangers.

They disembarked at Canal and Rampart. After entering through the stage door, Bill pointed out the room for the extras, though Mother and the girls knew it from rehearsals. Kay hesitated, looked up at him, and said nothing. He'd had to convince her to take part, and Pat being with her had given her a modicum of courage. Knowing she'd be nervous, he'd told her every person on stage would feel the same, even the leads. Helen wouldn't have been, but she was too young to control her natural flamboyance, something not wanted from the children in the crowd scenes. When he'd told Helen she couldn't participate, she'd accepted his pronouncement with a haughty, defiant look, and he'd felt no remorse. He smiled at Kay, and as soon as she turned her back, he headed to his station to test the pulleys and scrims a final time. He'd give her a wink when she entered with the rest for the processional.

AFTER the curtain calls, Bill readied his workspace for tomorrow's production. In the emptying parking lot, he found Uncle Dick's waiting car and fit himself into the one remaining spot. During the ride home, he was tired but exhilarated. With no outlet for the latter, he let the former overwhelm him and rested his cheek against the glass. Kay leaned against him. She and Pat had collapsed in the middle of the seat and were already dozing. Bill felt like joining them.

"Did Helen behave during the show?" Mother asked her sister.

Helen turned from her perch on Aunt Ethel's lap. "Of course I did. I'm not a baby."

"Congratulations, Bill," Uncle Dick said as he drove down St. Charles. "It was a great success. Too bad William couldn't get off work in time."

Bill couldn't resist a mild snort, though he felt Mother's glare against his back, her face certainly turned toward him as he kept his eyes on the brightly lit universities and mansions streaking across the window. Oh, no, we mustn't air our dirty laundry in public, not even in front of Daddy's brother. Resentment filled his chest, threatening to spill from his mouth. He rolled the window down further and gulped the cool night air.

"I want Daddy to come see me," said Kay. She wasn't asleep. Big ears and all that, Bill thought.

"He'll be at the next performance," Mother said firmly.

Bill couldn't resist a snide comment. "Will he be skipping church again?" The insinuation was flung into the air, and no one responded, not even Mother.

The DeSoto took the bend. No more big houses or faux Greek buildings housing aspiring graduates. At the red-brick library, Uncle Dick turned left. He pulled into the empty driveway. Ethel unloaded the sleeping Helen into Mother's arms, and Bill disentangled Kay from Pat.

He should've gone to the opening-night party, Bill thought. He immediately dismissed the idea. He pictured himself sitting in a chair in a corner, head and hands drooping, intimidated by the sopranos and tenors throwing their arms around one another—as they were wont to do when they weren't glaring at each other—the excess of emotion on display creating unease inside him. He knew he was appreciated by the company, but in the way a delivery boy was when he dropped off the bread and tea.

THE WEEKLY radio program from the Met ended with the words "conducted by Geoffrey Toye," and Bill sat up in excitement. "Surely we're related to him."

"I doubt it. There are many with the Toye name we're not related to." Daddy didn't add, because everyone in the family knew, that that included the owners of the local Toye Brothers Yellow Cab Company.

Bill didn't care about not being related to taxi drivers, but he refused to believe they weren't related to Sir Geoffrey. His own talent must come from the same wellspring. At eighteen, Bill had devised the sets for a major opera, though granted it was held in a minor city. It had been only six years since the city's new Opera Association had formed, but opera had been in the city's DNA since 1796. New Orleans had been a premier city for opera, and he would help it achieve its former glory. Bill sat down to write a letter.

The return mail brought him a kind refusal. The powers that be ignored his saying he was referred by Francis Toye, Geoffrey's brother. The letter implied he was too young; his resume was not long enough. It ended by gently suggesting an apprenticeship as a stagehand. Even if Bill hadn't thought that was beneath him, he knew there was no money to get him to New York—certainly no one to house him even if he could scrape up the fare. He didn't know anyone in the area. His Irish ancestors, including Daddy, hadn't gone through New York; they'd arrived in Canada before moving to Detroit and then making their way to New Orleans.

Perhaps he should've forged a letter with Francis's signature when he'd applied. Too risky, he thought. He'd forged parental excuses for school, but he didn't know Francis's handwriting, and the man himself could've been asked about its legitimacy. Yet what would he have lost if he'd done it? Nothing. He'd remember that for next time.

HE WENT to bed with a vision of glitter and sparkle emanating from stage lights. In a black-and-white photograph he'd found in a library volume on the history of opera, light shone on serried rows of men and women dressed in their finest—their white faces visible above their dark bodies, the conductor in the pit facing the musicians, ready for the swell. He himself felt ready for the swell; the music, tumescent then steady, drowned out everything else.

10

UNCLE BILL underwent electroconvulsive therapy (ECT), "shock treatment," more than once. My mother never said why. I've imagined his hearing voices and his obsessive working. His grandiose delusions become clearer as he gets older, and I've imagined its first instance as well. He left school at sixteen; perhaps mental illness had something to do with his being a poor student, which he admits he was in a lengthy 2010 *Garden & Gun* feature called "The Talented Mr. Toye."[2]

Aida was staged by the New Orleans Opera Association in the city's Municipal Auditorium. A 1949 article in the *Times-Picayune* states that Bill, at eighteen, is "so interested in the theater that he offered to secure 130 men and boys" for the second act's "Triumphal March," "when the elephants walk onto the stage."[3] I don't know if he delivered on what he promised. Nine days before the date of the first performance, he seems to have less than half that number. My mother told the story of being an extra in the crowd scenes of *Aida* numerous times, but she only mentioned Bill working on the sets—not that he was in charge of recruiting extras, only that he'd recruited his sister and cousin. The article also says he has "all the children (between 8 and 14) necessary." My mom would've been eleven years old and her cousin Pat twelve. My grandmother was a seamstress and made the girls' costumes for their one and only opera appearance, but I don't know if she was allowed backstage.

As an older child, I'd flipped through opera records in my grandparents' home, including an album displaying a caricature of a heavyset, tuxedoed man on its cover. I understood that these were Uncle Bill's records, though this wasn't his half of the house, and that he was an opera aficionado. In the *Garden & Gun* article, Bill says he was a stagehand at the age of seventeen at the Metropolitan Opera. I've never heard a family story about it. He believed the family was related to the renowned musical Toyes, though there's no evidence for it. Those Toyes were English. The Scots-Irish family I'm descended from had the last letter added to their surname when they arrived in America, though my mother didn't know why. The surname is Toy on my grandfather's birth certificate from 1894. I wonder if the added *e* was an affectation of my great-grandparents; perhaps my uncle inherited part of his eccentricity from them.

Not long after writing memoir sections to connect to my fictional sections, I told a good friend, a researcher and writer, about my new process; she recommended I reread Mary McCarthy's *Memories of a Catholic Girlhood*. I'd read it for a university course and loved it, but that was over thirty-five years ago. I read it again the next night and was startled by how I had "stolen" some of McCarthy's technique. Did I pull this method from somewhere deep in the recesses of my mind? I couldn't begin to figure out which books of the many I've read may have influenced me in one way or another.

After reading further into *Memories of a Catholic Girlhood*, in the chapter titled "A Tin Butterfly," I was reminded of my theory about the possible pretentions of my great-grandparents: "Our family, like many Irish Catholic new-rich families, was filled with aristocratic delusions; we children were always being told that we were descended from the kings of Ireland." My mother's family was not new-rich, or even old-rich. My mother could hardly get through *Angela's Ashes*: It was too much like her family's life; she found nothing funny in any of the dark humor Frank McCourt used to lighten his tragic tale. But when Paul and Michael, my two youngest brothers, went to visit Bill and Beryl in their nursing home a year or so after their sentencing, Beryl told them they were descended from Irish princes—pointing to a section of a book on Irish nobility, as if that were definitive proof.

11

Model Homes

THE CONSTANT HARPING rang in Bill's ears. What did Mother want from him? He'd studied on his own; he could build detailed models—ones of his own inventions even. After glancing at the glossy pages of an art book, he could copy the masters: Botticelli, Holbein, Vermeer. He'd written letters to local engineering and architectural firms, elaborating on his sets for the New Orleans Opera and including a story of his time at the Met, describing the lowliest of jobs.

As if it were suitable for framing, someone had folded the newspaper to a full-page advertisement showing Daddy and another man holding bottles of Jax, touting the beer as being the city's best. Daddy must've been in the right place at the right time—likely a bar, likely charming a sales representative—to get the gig. Bill had to admit Daddy looked handsome in the photo. His bright eyes, smile, and straight white teeth shone through the black-and-white graininess. Bill scoffed at Daddy being called an "engineer," and he wondered if the other man was truly a "pharmaceutist" or if that was another trick with words.

Bill thrust the newspaper aside and dreamed again of sleeping on the floor in any empty space he could find in the massive building taking up an entire New York city-block—envisioning the Met's gorgeous interior, a seat he couldn't afford, the cramped backstage filled with panels he'd slide on and off the stage, hiding behind them to catch a few hours of sleep. The mail brought him some quick rejections and, finally, an encouraging letter from Wolpert and Associates inviting him to call for an appointment.

BILL knocked on the door, left ajar as usual, and strode into Mr. Wolpert's office, gently placing the rolled-up blueprint on his modest-sized desk. Mr. Wolpert looked up, confused. "Finished already?"

Bill stood with his hands locked behind his back. "I hope you have a minute to come see it."

Mr. Wolpert pushed his chair away and, as they left the office, his hand lingered on Bill's back. Bill tried not to cringe—forcing himself to stand up straight, reminding himself to act like the others—as they walked the short distance to his workspace. Bill felt the lack of Mr. Wolpert's hand and turned to look at the older man. Mr. Wolpert's eyes blinked behind his glasses. He moved closer and crouched down to view the details. He shook his head and stood up straight; he was inches shorter than Bill. "This is a marvel. I have no idea how you did it so quickly and in such fine detail."

"Thank you, sir." Everyone was always surprised at how fast he worked. As with his paintings, all he had to do was look at photographs in a book— or, in this case, blueprints—and his fingers worked independently of his mind. He executed his reproductions with speed and precision, and he didn't think about it.

"The client will be pleased. Have Tony move it to Engineering." Mr. Wolpert stuck out his hand and, after a moment of hesitation, Bill clasped it. "Congratulations. You've passed your first test with the highest grade."

After Mr. Wolpert left, Bill pulled out a handkerchief. Sweat had broken out on his forehead, and he wiped his brow. He'd passed this test, but there was always the next.

WHEN not making architectural models for Mr. Wolpert's firm, Bill threw himself into painting, especially on sleepless nights. He'd studied Renoir, Gauguin, Sisley, and Monet, burning through the books at home and those in the library too. With his own spending money, he sent off for more books from New York, their full-page, glossy reproductions exactly what he needed. After knocking off reproductions of Sisley's *The Church at Moret* series, Monet's *The Artist's House at Argenteuil*, and even Degas's *Semiramis Building Babylon*, he gave them away indiscriminately to Mother and to Aunt Ethel, who'd immediately hung them on their walls; and to the postman and the delivery boys, who'd lingered at the door looking for monetary tips but left with paintings they were told were valuable.

"ARE you a commie?"

Bill gave his most affable smile. "I'm an American. Just like you. And of course I'm not a communist. I support a candidate who cares about the individual." He leaned toward Stan, his coworker; they were about the same age, and Bill wondered why Stan had such reactionary ideas. "Somewhere down the line, your father, or your grandfather, was discriminated against for being a Polack."

Stan shifted away from Bill, looked at the floor. "C'mon, Ike is a war hero."

"I'm not against Eisenhower, but his war record doesn't make him presidential material. And his party's fear-mongering isn't what I'd call American. Demagoguery is the danger, not the unlikely threat of communism."

Stan looked up, looked Bill in the eye. "You're backing a losing cause. Your man will never be president."

Discouraged, Bill thought of Adlai Stevenson's professorial demeanor, and he picked up the petition from Stan's desk, bidding him goodnight. At twenty-one, one of the youngest members of Volunteers for Stevenson, he wanted to stand out, yet he couldn't get his own parents to sign the petition. The deadline was tonight. The newspaper advertisement he'd shared the expenses for was going to press in the morning. The approximately one hundred signatures they'd collected did not seem enough.

That night the group met in the Carrollton home of the female cochairman, Mrs. Bruhn. She set out sandwiches and tea, and Bill was grateful for the refreshments, as otherwise he'd forget to eat.

"The Negro GOP club in town has thrown their allegiance to Stevenson," Vice-Chairman Kerry told the gathered Volunteers. "Once Dewey decided he wasn't running again, they changed their name to the Ralph Bernal Democratic Club. They're against Ike that much. Of course, I can't blame them."

"Who's Bernal?" asked a young man Bill didn't know. Someone else had been able to recruit a new member.

"A Republican leader, in the Seventh Ward. Died a couple of years ago."

"Was he a black man?"

"Of course. The whole Seventh Ward is Creole."

"How do we fill up a full-page ad with only a hundred signatures?" Mrs. Adkin, the group's secretary, lamented over their rough copy.

Bill had come up with a solution as he'd walked to the Bruhn home. "With more of our platform," he answered, ripping a sheet from the legal pad on the coffee table. He wrote, paragraph after paragraph, on Stevenson's opposition to communism, on his foreign policy—noting Eisenhower's resorting to platitudes, adding a final paragraph about Ike's greatness as a soldier but not as a politician. He didn't notice the raised eyebrows and quizzical looks circling the silent room as the others waited for him to finish.

The page was passed around. He accepted the compliments and, graciously, a few minor edits. Mrs. Adkin typed the final draft, and the meeting broke up with smiles and handshakes.

As Bill walked home, he surveyed the tops of the water oaks, the roofs of the raised homes, and felt he could scale those heights. He anticipated a sleepless night, but he wasn't worried. He'd paint the night away.

Several sleepless nights led to an inevitable crash, and one morning he didn't get up for work. No amount of coaxing from Mother could get him out the door. He made it to the table once and sipped a cup of tea, but was incapable of washing and getting dressed, much less leaving the house. He smelled sour, the sweat breaking out all over his body mingling with the odor of unclean sheets; his breath was rank and labored. When he finally lay exhausted, Mother dabbed at his brow and cheeks, and washed his hands with mild soap on a damp washrag; otherwise he thrashed at her, not wanting to be touched.

Mother called the firm and made excuses for him. Mr. Wolpert was concerned, polite, then bemused at the thought of his bottom line, eventually saying they had to move on without him.

12

During my research, I came across a print advertisement in the *Times-Picayune* with the caption "The whole town's saying: 'Finest Jax Ever Brewed!'"[4] Even if the ad hadn't included my grandfather's name, I would've immediately recognized him—especially his smile, lips parted in welcome and conviviality.

Bill's name is among those listed in the Volunteers for Stevenson ad in the *Times-Picayune*.[5] The names of my politically engaged grandparents are not, nor are the names of any other Toye family members. A statement below the names reads, "We wish to express our regret to the scores of others who would have liked to sign, but whom, in the pressure of time, we did not reach, and to those whose signatures reached us too late for inclusion." To my ear that sounds like something my uncle would've thought of: a stretched truth or a downright lie.

13

Asylums

THE DAY CAME, again, when Daddy and Uncle Dick helped Bill out the side door and into the back seat of the DeSoto. Mother followed with an overnight bag for the hospital while Kay cried, and Helen and Wayne looked on—the former clinically, the latter sympathetically as if remembering when he was a baby and needed to be carried. Dressed in their Catholic-school uniforms, the three walked down the block, Helen and Wayne to the elementary school at the corner and Kay to the streetcar stop. The streetcar took her around the bend and down St. Charles Avenue to Willow Street, where she walked down leafy blocks to the school that resembled a church and was her present refuge.

After school, Kay took the same streetcar line in reverse, passing up the Plum Street stop, continuing a few more blocks to work as a cashier at McKenzie's Bakery, a local chain. On Saturdays she walked to save the fare. She liked her job but preferred working on Saturdays, even though she had to get up with the crowing of the cock that lived in a neighbor's back yard—everyone else sleeping in, Mother walking into the kitchen as Kay left through the side door. On weekday afternoons, the kind of boys Mother warned her about—young men, really—came into the bakery. Sleepy-eyed, they bought the last of the stale doughnuts, along with some of the always-fresh coffee. A strange scent wrapped its tendrils around them, not of tobacco but something sweeter, something she'd never tell Mother about. The worldly girls at school gossiped about a funny kind of cigarette; one of the girls, a known liar, professed she'd smoked one once.

The ducktailed boys, unlike the crewcut Daddy and Bill, wore loafers and turned-up jeans and, worst of all, cigarette packs rolled in the sleeves of their T-shirts. They flirted with her and she didn't know how to respond, except to ring up their purchases and hand them their change, avoiding their eyes. The only thing she felt confident about was her math; she'd

become an expert at sliding each needed coin down and out of its cate-
gorized pocket, tallying out loud so they knew she wasn't cheating them.
She dropped the coins in their outstretched hollowed palms, making
sure her fingers never touched, though once she was tempted to drop
the tip of her index finger to test the reaction of one boy who was polite
and wore no cigarettes. She didn't dare.

By the time Kay left the bakery, it was dark, the winter skies falling
early, and she took the streetcar home instead of walking. Even with Bill
in the hospital, dinner would be ready; afterward she'd help Mother tidy
the kitchen. On a normal evening—not one suffused with Bill's trou-
bles—if Daddy wasn't working, her parents would then sit in the front
room, reading bits from the newspaper to each other. Kay loved hearing
their confident talk, and several pieces of information stuck to her as she
finished her homework or studied for exams. She'd learned more from
them about Louisiana politics than from any teacher or schoolbook.
One of Mother's favorite expressions was about a little knowledge being
a dangerous thing.

Daddy had told Kay that long before others realized what Huey P.
Long had been up to, Mother had despised the late senator. Many who'd
worshipped him had come around to her point of view, but the negative
effects of much he'd done lived on. Mother railed against his name being
plastered on bridges and roads while pointing out how much the enter-
prises had cost, hidden expenses still being rooted out. Kay's mind glazed
over when Bill and Helen entered the conversations, Helen's contributions
esoteric and Bill's contradictory. Her siblings raised their voices; their
words devolved into scoffing and mocking until they retreated to their
separate corners of the dining table. Kay preferred them there, obsessed
and silent with their individual interests.

Neither Helen nor Bill seemed to care that there was no privacy in
the house; they expressed themselves as they felt fit, with no shame or
embarrassment. Many times, Kay wanted a release but was too proud
to let Mother hear or see her tears, especially as Mother was usually the
cause of Kay's distress. As a senior, Kay was permitted by her high school
to wear lipstick, but Mother still wouldn't allow it. A pink cylinder lived
deep down in Kay's purse under a huge wad of tissue, which she used to
scrub off the color before leaving school for the day. If Kay had run into
a neighbor at the bakery or on her commute, they might've betrayed

her. Mother tolerated no debates about her rules. She was as absolute as Huey Long.

INSIDE the museum, Bill wandered away from his family, who were intensely scrutinizing every facet of Helen's painting. It portrayed a young woman sitting in a chair, the colors bold and intense. He hadn't cast a glance at Helen, but he'd sensed the seventeen-year-old's smugness at having a painting hanging in the Delgado Museum of Art, a perk for the youthful winners of a statewide contest. Mother complained that the newspaper had listed Helen as one of the winners from outside New Orleans; it was her school that was outside the city, across the Pontchartrain. Why Helen couldn't have gone to the same high school Kay had attended, Bill didn't understand; but she'd received a full scholarship, including room and board, and he admitted it was a relief to have one less person in the house.

In a room off the main hall, colorful paintings caught his eye. A short biography stated they belonged to a Negro woman living on a northern Louisiana plantation. The deepness of a big sky, yellow between peaked white clouds like lemon slices and frothed cream on a blue plate, was compelling, but the figures too simple. He disdained this kind of primitivism. He could barely tolerate Gauguin, whose works he found garish and blocky. With Gauguin he could at least see talent, which was not evident in this woman. He could've done this as a child. He had done better as a child.

14

In a letter dated January 19, 1956, written from my grandmother to my mother while the latter was on a high school trip as a senior, she first chastises her daughter for not giving "a little news of your trip" in the "two short letters" she'd received from her. The trip to New York was famous in Mama's memory for being the first time she saw snow. It was also the first time she was away from home; Grandma Toye must've allowed it because nuns were chaperoning. Near the end of the letter, before signing it "Mother," she writes, "I worked at the polls with Billy Tuesday, all day. Morrison lost, so I hate to think of old New Orleans with Earl Long." Earl Long was Huey's younger brother. In that gubernatorial election, Earl easily bested Mayor of New Orleans deLesseps "Chep" Morrison; "Billy" was twenty-four at the time.

According to the *Times-Picayune*, Helen was a winner of an annual Louisiana Youth Concerts Art Contest when she was a senior in high school.[6] The winners' paintings were displayed at the Delgado Museum, now called the New Orleans Museum of Art (NOMA). Clementine Hunter's work was on display in a solo exhibition at the same museum in 1955. I imagined it still hanging there a few years later when Bill could've gone to view his sister's painting. He told the writer of the *Garden & Gun* feature that Hunter's work was "junk" and "only good as dartboards."

15

A Prospective Home

"THERE'S NO NEED TO WORRY." Mother straightened the temples of her eyeglasses as she looked up from her sewing.

Kay had always pleaded school and work when her mother said she should learn to sew. She'd never had an interest in sitting down with Mother, knowing she'd feel trapped by her presence and bound by her threads. Now that she and Ted were serious, she envisioned sewing him a bathrobe, baby gowns and girly dresses for their future children. But night classes, her first semester at the university, and working 9 to 5 at an insurance company as receptionist and assistant to the owner didn't leave much time for anything else. "But what about Bill and Daddy?"

Mother stood up. Her posture was ramrod straight, as usual, and she'd come to expect it of her girls too. Kay and Helen had embraced the expectation and practiced with telephone books, giggling when the volumes fell off the tops of their heads. Mother had given up on Bill, who hunched his shoulders as if to make himself less conspicuous. "Bill is fine right now. You know he is." She looked Kay directly in the eyes. "I'll talk to Daddy. He's speaking at the DBE meeting this evening. If he can hold it together for the Daughters of the British Empire, he can certainly do so for his own daughter."

"Daddy's not British." Incredulous, Kay knew her father scorned being labeled as such.

"He met one of the husbands when he was out." Mother accentuated the last word. The euphemism did not need to be explained. "They want to hear about any immigrant experience from the area. Have you explained the situation to Ted?"

"Not yet." Kay fidgeted with a spool of thread Mother had left on the corner of the table. She looked up at her mother. "I will. I'll do it tomorrow."

"I'll make sure of Daddy for Sunday dinner." She looked her daughter straight in the eyes again. "Invite Ted for church. He does go to church, doesn't he?"

"Oh, yes. He said his parents, especially his mother, are very devout. They attend Sacred Heart. He was an altar boy there and thought of going into the priesthood, though that was when he was quite young."

Mother nodded and sat down again. Couldn't she smile more, Kay wondered. She understood no one else might go through the house whistling jauntily like Daddy, but if only he could allocate some of his smiles to his wife.

"Mrs. Palmisano is coming for a fitting tomorrow. I must get this done." The quiet whirring of the sewing machine accompanied Kay as she got ready for bed. She knew she'd have trouble sleeping, but it was the only thing left to do.

USUALLY, after a Saturday-night bender, Daddy got up in time for church and napped afterward. Warned ahead of time, he'd behaved himself and was able to sit in the front room and watch the football game with Ted. How typical of him, Bill thought, to save his best behavior for outsiders. His long legs stretched out, Wayne lay on the floor in front of the TV, intently watching. Bill had no interest in the game, though he tried to follow the other men's conversation. "Johnny U is the best. How many touchdowns has he thrown this season?" "Thirty-something, at least ten more than Conerly." "Whew, no one will ever surpass that." "Unless it's Unitas himself." The two men laughed easily, and Bill caught Wayne grinning.

Before leaving, with Kay smiling at his side, Ted shook hands with the men, joked with Wayne about his height, and complimented Mother once again on the meal. Daddy then had a Sunday-night binge instead of the usual Saturday one. At least Kay's young man was spared the sight of his homecoming.

WOULD wonders never cease, Bill thought. With Kay and Ted engaged to be married soon, Daddy was attending Alcoholics Anonymous meetings. Unusually for a weekend, Daddy was neither drunk nor hungover, though his hands—large with long fingers like Bill's own—were shaking. If Daddy could attempt sobriety now, he could've done it sooner. His stated reason for going to AA—the prospect of grandchildren—couldn't make that much of a difference. Did his own children not matter one whit? The only childhood memories Bill had of Daddy were of his sloppy drunkenness. And the cleaning up, both literally and figuratively, that Mother imposed on all of them after every incident.

Daddy's copy of the so-called Big Book was tucked under his chair. The triangle-within-a-circle on the book's cover was a matter of family amusement. Joking that it was an occult symbol was their way of expressing relief that Daddy was serious about quitting drinking. Even Mother joined in the jest, though at first she was skeptical. Daddy had explained its meaning: the three points of recovery, unity, and service, within the circle of the world. To maintain sobriety, members were encouraged to find a "higher power," and knowing Daddy had never lacked for such within the Catholic Church, Mother was content. AA's use of the Serenity Prayer, even in a modified form, eased her mind that the fellowship was not some sort of cult.

A baseball game was on the TV. All Bill could discern was that it was game 4 of the World Series, and that Daddy and Ted were pulling for the Yankees. There was some talk of the M&M boys, and even Bill knew they weren't talking about candy, though lately that seemed to be a big topic as well, with color now being added to the candies' coatings. Bill felt a perverse, though silent, pleasure when Pittsburgh won. The Pirates had tied up the series. He'd heard enough to know that.

Mother had been working on Kay's wedding dress for days. She and Kay were at Aunt Ethel's with the dress, so Ted couldn't get a glimpse of it. Bill thought that unnecessary; anyone could see Ted was only interested in the game. As soon as it was over, Bill led him to the dining table and unrolled some old blueprints as an example of what he could do. "Let me know what you want, and I'll draw it up. It'll be my wedding present to you and Kay."

Ted thanked him profusely, shook his hand, and told him as soon as he was ready to build, he'd let him know. Right now all he required was a rental, but once Bill's nieces and nephews started arriving, they'd need his services.

Ethel and Helen (Grandma Toye), 1922

Grandpa Toye with Billy and Kay, November 1938

Grandma Toye with Billy and Kay,
November 1938

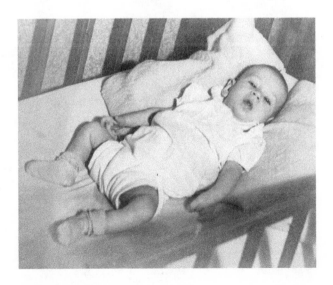

Philip Toye, August 30, 1944

Billy and Dickie, 1940

Kay, circa 1954

Grandma Toye, 1954

Grandpa Toye, date unknown

Teresa and brothers (right to left) Ted, Kevin, and Paul, February 1966

16

SHORTLY AFTER MY BROTHER PAUL, the fourth child, was born, we moved from a small two-bedroom house in the Lakeview area of New Orleans over the 17th Street Canal to a new four-bedroom house Uncle Bill had designed for my parents. It would be my mother's home for the next forty years. Its rolled-up, rubber-banded blueprints were propped in a corner of my dad's study, which was off the kitchen. After my mother's death in 2015, I found them—or what I thought was them—in a different house, the one she'd bought after the 2005 levee breaches of Hurricane Katrina had put a foot of canal water into our longtime home. The whole of 2005 was rough for all of us. After a lengthy debilitating illness, my father died, two months before Hurricane Katrina hit. I didn't look at the prints for years.

As I finally unroll the blueprints, the paper delicate and tearing at the edges, I notice Mama had penciled on its outer edge the street name of my paternal grandparents' house and the words "done by William James Toye." I realize these blueprints are not of my family home, and I have to adjust the belief I've held all these years. Once again, I ponder the assumptions we make based on incomplete knowledge. Our surname and "May 1961" are written on an inner edge of the paper in what looks like my dad's printing. After completely unrolling the blueprints, I notice Uncle Bill's handwriting resembles my mother's. His drawings are elegant. By May 1961, my parents had been married for three months, and I would be born in seven. It seems my dad took advantage of Bill's abilities sooner than I fictionally envisioned.

If the blueprints of our family home had remained on the floor of Daddy's study, they would've been ruined in the floodwaters. Perhaps the ones in my possession had been on a shelf in the closet. When I was about eleven or so, I'd rummage around, searching for treasure among my father's law, banking, and taxation books. I found a small Latin textbook and, surprisingly, novels like *Marjorie Morningstar* and *Lorna Doone*.

With my father at work, sitting in his office in another building, and my siblings and Mama in other parts of the house, I'd sit in his study and skim the novels, looking for the "good parts." I knew I was too young for them. When anyone stuck their head in the doorway, wondering what I was doing, I'd close the book and pretend I was watching the portable TV, tuned to something different than what was on in the den.

17

A Divided House

BILL MANAGED TO KEEP body and mind together during the ceremony. He tried not to slump in the few photos he was required to be in and especially not when he walked his mother down the aisle of Mater Dolorosa, a church he'd attended since childhood. He didn't realize till then how long its center aisle was. The church of the Sorrowful Mother, not appropriate for his own on this day—Mother smiled more today than he'd ever seen her do before. It was the opposite for Daddy, losing his favorite child as well as, Bill imagined, fighting the urge to drink, especially at the reception when the champagne was brought out, though that kind of classy drink was never Daddy's vice.

Back home after the wedding, Bill flopped in a chair pulled out from the dining table. He thought of how even with Kay gone, the house wouldn't seem empty enough until Helen was gone too. Monday couldn't come soon enough for Bill, when she'd be back at work and night school. It was easier then, not having to listen to her contrariness or see her artistic endeavors. The space she, her typewriter, and easel took up should've been his. Helen had given the newly married couple a set of landscapes she'd painted: an Irish castle on a hill overlooking the countryside, white and black animal-shapes within a gated enclosure; the other, buildings crowded along and streaming outward from the Tiber River, two towers pointing toward a yellow-streaked sky, Vatican City in the background. Amateurish, Bill thought, the greens lush but too dark, reminding him of no other artist he'd studied. Helen's originality was not something he admired. When Helen had presented the paintings to Kay in this very room, he'd walked in on Kay saying she'd cherish them forever.

"That's something I'll never go through," Helen said now as she sat across from him in the other chair at the table, a glass of cola in her hand. Her wedding finery—a short dark-blue veiled head-covering (needed

59

for church if not for fashion), dyed-blue silk pumps, and a light-blue full-skirted dress with a cinched waist—had been discarded. After finishing Kay's dress, Mother had sewn all the bridesmaids' dresses. Fresh from a bath, Helen was in her dingy white robe.

"Marriage or a ceremony?" Bill asked. She'd managed to stir his curiosity, or maybe he merely wanted to know how long he'd be stuck with her.

"Both." She snorted. "But don't worry, big brother. After I graduate, I won't be coming back here." The ice cubes tinkled as she raised the glass to her lips.

In one sentence Bill felt as if she'd read his mind and accused him of something. "Do you think I'll be staying here my whole life? I have plans too." Bill's fingers tapped the table. Conversation with his baby sister was frustrating. It was never like that with Kay.

"What might those be? Will you ever make enough to support yourself with your *models*?" She stressed the final word, a scornful emphasis as if speaking of toys.

"I don't need to justify myself to you." Bill pushed away from the table, trying not to give her the satisfaction that she'd gotten his goat.

Helen smiled her irritating smile. "True, but there's always Mother." She snorted again, and Bill wondered if there was something else besides cola and ice in her tumbler. He wouldn't put it past her, though where in this house, with its few compartments containing a mishmash of everyone's clothes, she'd hide a bottle he had no idea. Alcohol held no interest for him. He'd seen too much of its effects, and the few times he'd sampled it, it had no impact on his teeming brain.

"I can always go back to New York. I've kept up with my contacts there, and with Francis Toye. I could go to London, work at Covent Garden."

Helen's eyes widened. She set down her drink. "Don't let Mother hear you say that. She'll send you back for more shock."

Bill stood and looked down on her. "Speaking of Mother," he snarled, "you better be careful with whatever it is you have in your glass." Helen gave him another irritating smile then a dismissive wave of fingers from a hand still wrapped around the glass as she drained its dregs.

AFTER filing the appropriate paperwork at City Hall, Bill contacted the newspaper to announce his candidacy. He described himself as the owner of a technical and market research firm. He didn't say he'd had only one client so far—his brother-in-law—but it was the truth: He'd filed incorporation papers before throwing his hat into the proverbial ring. Confident in his knowledge of local politics, he knew to start small. The District-A seat of the city council was a good beginning. With the support of some of the now-disbanded Volunteers of Stevenson, he ignored skeptical looks from naysayers. He curried favor from his church group and the two business associations he'd joined. The newspaper listed his attendance at the university, though he hadn't mentioned to the reporter it had been for a single, unfinished semester.

"That's a handsome picture the paper ran of you." Aunt Ethel congratulated him in front of the house. He was impatient to get inside, to grab a sandwich if there were any leftovers, to contemplate strategy. He'd been at the main library, reading about campaign operations. Surrounded by books and journals, he'd looked up in confusion when he was asked by a librarian to leave. The library was closing. He'd been there all day, not once noting the time, or hunger and thirst. He realized Aunt Ethel was still talking. "I've been stumping for you, at the Sodality of Our Lady, at—"

Bill cut her off before she could list the rest of the Catholic groups she belonged to; unlike Mother, Aunt Ethel had time for socializing. "Thank you. I'll need the grassroots help. Good night."

"NASH says the hurricane's going to hit us—a direct hit." Daddy snapped the newspaper as he gestured toward the television. "So much for coverage of Koufax's perfect game."

"Where's Kay going to be?" Helen asked Mother as she came into the front room.

"They're staying put." Moving a section of the newspaper aside, Mother sat in her chair. "Thank goodness Wayne is training in Texas and not at Keesler, or even in Mobile." Upon graduating from high school, Wayne had joined the Air National Guard. Keesler was smack-dab on the Mississippi Gulf Coast, and the city of Mobile was the gateway to the Alabama Gulf Coast. Both were in Betsy's projected path.

"Our stock of patron-saint candles will see us through." Bill chuckled. A row of devotional candles lived in the chifforobe, the glass clanking any time the drawer was opened and closed. "Saint Expeditus was completely consumed the last time the power failed. Has anyone replaced him?" That the electricity returned soon after the red vigil-candle burned itself out was a source of amusement to Bill. With nothing to do but talk in the darkness of that outage, he'd regaled his family with the story of the nuns at Our Lady of Guadalupe on Rampart Street mistaking the word on a crate's label—*Expédit*—for the name of the saintly statue shipped to them. "Without him I think we'll be in for a long stretch." Bill chuckled again. He was as pious as the next man, but he prided himself on not being superstitious.

It was the scariest evening in their memory of hurricanes. Wind whipped and rattled the windows they'd taped over in preparation for the storm. No one slept. At one point Helen joked they should hide under the table. At that, they wondered how Kay was doing, recalling her fear during air-raid drills when the students had to hunker under their desks. When the eye passed over, the relative calm of the breezes was even eerier; an hour later as the winds frothed up again and the house shook, they wished for that unnerving calm.

In the small hours it was over, but no one went outside until the early sun shed its weak rays downward. Water lapped the porch steps. A neighborhood boy rowed a canoe down the street. The telephone worked, and they called Kay, who said she and her family were fine, though the conditions were the same in her suburb.

The electricity was out for a week. The running water in the house hadn't failed, so the full bathtub wasn't needed. Mother cooked the defrosted chicken and pork on the gas stove, and they had some for every meal, even breakfast. They were thoroughly sick of meat, and one another, by the time the waters receded and the power returned.

BECAUSE Hurricane Betsy hit the Ninth Ward harder than any other part of New Orleans, that area drew most of the city's attention afterward. During his campaign, Bill objected to the Carrollton area being neglected, though government inattention had been a fact long before the storm. At speaking engagements and to the newspaper, he contrasted the quick rebuilding and new construction in the Central Business District and in the suburbs with the "stagnation" in "our older historic heart of New Orleans."[7]

He shook hands and listened to his potential constituents—leaning back on his heels, hearing Mother's exhortation to stand tall. He threw his support to the juvenile court system when asked by the League of

Women Voters about increased salaries for counselors. He went one step further, recommending college placement programs for juvenile offenders. Again, it was there for all to see in the newspaper.

Bill stayed home to view the election results with his parents on their black-and-white set. He came in third out of three, with not even two thousand votes to his credit. Unfortunately, on November 12, that was also in the paper for all to see: "Schiro Certified as Winner; Councilman District A: Henry B. Curtis . . . 27,955; Louis W. Schiekau . . . 2,214; William J. Toye . . . 1,883." He blamed his huge loss on the liberal causes he'd championed and decided to abandon politics.

ALMOST a full year after the election, on a late-October Sunday morning, he stood at the bottom of the church steps with his parents as they talked to Father Kelly. Nearby, other parishioners lingered on the sidewalk—chatting, enjoying the mild weather, as if in anticipation of an autumn that didn't always arrive. Bill was having one of his good days. He'd slept well: no voices keeping him awake, no obsessions running through his brain.

"How old is Kay's youngest now?" Father Kelly asked.

Bill knew Mother was calculating in her head. "He was born in 1965, April, so that makes him almost two."

He wondered if most grandmothers had to figure out their grandchildren's ages. He gave her some credit in that Kay and Ted's brood had increased quickly—four children in six years. The family was now living in the four-bedroom house Bill had designed. Even though it was in a suburb—a place foreign to Bill, who rarely ventured out of the city—he was pleased they were pleased. At least Ted had the good sense to locate it only one interstate exit into suburbia. He'd said something about not getting caught in the rush-hour traffic that would come as the suburbs were built up.

Bill's thoughts were arrested by the appearance of a young woman at Father Kelly's side. She wore a short, swingy skirt, and her legs, in seamless nylons, ended in almost childlike T-strap sandals. Their heels were lower than on the shoes most women wore, the toe not rounded but coming to a point as if in exclamation. Dark bangs lay smoothly across her forehead, and her head was topped with a mantilla that gave an exotic cast to her features. The headscarves on the other women were plain and serviceable, and Bill hadn't given a thought to them before now. As she smiled at the priest, she gracefully removed the lacy scarf and draped it over her arm. The revealed hairstyle was different than that of most girls. Even the unconventional Helen wore hers straight to the shoulders and flipped up at the ends. This young woman sported a shorter coiffure, curled fully around the ears and neck.

"Here is the Toye family I was telling you about," Father Kelly said. "Mr. Toye, Mrs. Toye, this is Beryl Spaulding. She comes to us from England. I've assured her you will be kind to her even though William was born in Ireland." Everyone chuckled. "Beryl, this is Bill Toye, the young man who may know more about opera than even you." Hands were shaken all around and Bill, left for last, imagined that Beryl's lingered longer in his. Though she was slightly built, *fullness* was the word Bill couldn't stop hearing in his head.

"Mr. Toye, you must be related to the illustrious Sir Geoffrey Toye, though he is English." Beryl's hands were clasped in front of her, as if she were giving elocution lessons.

Before Daddy could answer, Bill intervened. "We are." He looked into Beryl's eyes, willing her not to look at his incredulous parents, who scoffed at his insistence that they were related to the legendary conductor.

"I knew it. I could tell by the way you carry yourself," Beryl said to Bill. "I wouldn't be surprised if you're also descended from Irish princes."

Bill spoke quickly. "The relationship with Sir Geoffrey is a distant one, but it's a true one. Miss Spaulding—"

"Please call me Beryl."

Bill was overcome with a vulnerability he didn't understand, as if he were standing naked before them all, but he pressed on. "Beryl, do you live here—permanently, I mean?"

"I'll be staying another fortnight."

Bill's heart sank; he wondered if that would be enough time. He decided to express a certainty he didn't feel. "Excellent. The American National is in town with *Tosca*. Marie Collier has the lead. If you're interested, I would like to take you, as my guest."

"I'd be delighted." Beryl looked at his parents. "Perhaps I will see you next Sunday. It's been a pleasure meeting you." Mesmerized by the melodious accent coming from Beryl's lips, Bill hadn't stopped looking at them.

Ignoring his mother's sharp look, Bill's exultation carried him down the pavement. Halfway down the block, Daddy's voice called him back. "Son, why did you lie to that nice young woman? You know we're not English. My father was Scottish. He was a confectioner, and what's wrong with that?"

"I did not lie to Beryl." Already her name sounded familiar, something he possessed as a part of himself. "Your insistence that we are not related to Sir Geoffrey means nothing, except to show your prejudice."

Two weeks later Beryl had returned to England and Bill was bereft. He wrote letter after letter, wooing her with confident words, knowing she felt the same—they were the same. She'd recognized the greatness within him, and he needed only her to be able to show it to the world. Lifting his pen from the page, he thought about sending her a drawing. He'd love to give her the Monet he'd recently finished, but he decided to save it for their next meeting.

He set *Aida* on the turntable, the volume low in consideration of the sleepers. Humming along to the opening, he pulled out the plans for the controversial *Turandot* and spread them on the dining table. Puccini had died before completing the final act, his choice of composer to finish it vetoed by his son, though some critics found the whole opera flawed, not just its ending. With the pocket door closed, the room felt oppressive. He'd suggested Helen move her typewriter to the TV tray by the armchair in the front room, but she'd remained recalcitrant. Always in his way, she countered by telling him how he was in hers.

He knew if he tried to sleep, the overwhelming blackness behind his eyes as soon as he closed them would be disturbing, might even trigger a panic attack. A sinking into oblivion, so black it was purple, would have him struggling to swim up from the depths—his breathing shallow, his heart pounding. Instead, he'd sat up in his narrow bed and slipped his feet into his waiting loafers. When he'd turned on the overhead light in the dining room, his eyes had blinked at the sudden brightness. As much as he hated sleep's darkness, he wished illumination wasn't so harsh; a happy medium didn't seem to exist. At least in the electric light he didn't feel the presence of the other. And how infinitely better to have actual music streaming in his ears than to hear strains that never seemed to cease behind his closed eyelids.

Beryl's letters confirmed his feelings, not that he'd expected anything else. She made plans to return, agreeing they should marry as soon as possible. Father Kelly counseled that if they were sure—after having known each other such a short time—he'd marry them. He realized Bill at his age knew his own mind and Beryl, though ten years younger than Bill, knew hers. Beryl joked that her parents were relieved that she, at the ripe old age of twenty-six, was finally getting married.

Aunt Ethel and Uncle Dick no longer lived in the Plum Street home. After Pat married, they moved, selling their portion to Mother and Daddy. "I'm marrying Beryl, and I will require the other half of the house," Bill said to Mother now.

"Impossible. We need rent money to pay the mortgage."

"Daddy's job is steady."

"The salary of a night watchman will not cover our expenses. Not even with my sewing, not even if I have clients here from morning to night."

"I will pay you rent."

"That too seems impossible."

"I work for the Opera. I design buildings. What more do you want from me?"

"All of that is too haphazard. If you were someone I didn't know, I would deny your request based on your income."

"What about Helen?"

"You know this. She's back at school. She types papers for others. Yes, that too is haphazard, but I'll not deny her the opportunity to further her education."

Bill knew not to press further; the biggest point of contention between them was that he did not finish high school. It was hardly his fault. The shock treatments had left him feeble for months, as lifeless as Philip had been.

Several days later, knowing potential tenants were expected, Bill's hopes of waylaying them were fulfilled. Mother was shopping with Kay, who could now drive; Ted had taught her. It was Saturday, so presumably she'd left the children with him. Bill unlocked the front door to the couple's knock and faced them on the porch. "I'm sorry. The house has already been rented."

The man and woman wore their Sunday best, a dark fedora and a pillbox atop their respective heads. Did they think he couldn't see through them? "My wife spoke to a woman on the phone this morning. We're a bit early; I apologize for that."

"That was my mother. She's not well and doesn't remember things. I'm sorry for your trouble. If I could've gotten to the phone, I would've explained the situation to you. Please excuse me; I have much to do." He closed and bolted the door.

He'd been secretly moving, leaning his paraphernalia against the bare walls: models of various buildings, paintbrushes, pastels, oils, a blank canvas. After proprietarily inspecting his side of the house, he locked its front door and slipped the key into his pocket in time to see Kay's car coming down the street. As the car crunched into the oyster-shell driveway, he sauntered down the porch stairs and to his parents' side of the house. He helped Kay retrieve the brown paper bags from the back seat, and they entered through the side door, Mother holding it open for her two oldest.

The grocery bags were set on the dining-room table, then moved into the kitchen one by one for their contents to be put away. "I can't imagine what happened to the couple who called this morning," Mother said, putting the last tin Kay handed her into the food safe. "They assured me they'd be here by eleven on the dot. It's a quarter past."

"You can't rely on these people," Bill said from the dining room, "but I promise you can depend on me. I've already moved some things over."

"Did you send them away?" Mother's voice was unforgiving, "How dare you? This household cannot be maintained without rent money."

Mother pulled out a chair from the kitchen table and sat down. Her eyes bored into Bill's. He didn't flinch from her unwavering stare. Uncomfortable at any sign of conflict, Kay averted her gaze to the backdoor window with its white-painted wooden muntins dividing the view of the fig tree into quadrants. Mother's presence filled the kitchen; Bill's tall frame filled the doorway leading to the dining room. With no other exit available to her, Kay turned the backdoor key. She winced at the screen door's creakiness. She'd pick some figs to calm her nerves, though they were probably not ripe yet.

Kay pulled a wrought-iron chair under the tree and sat down. She fiddled with the plastic bowl kept on an outside wooden shelf—now in her lap, empty. Lifting her face to the leaves, she thought how happy she was to be out of this shotgun house. She hadn't minded sharing a room with Helen, but how many people had to share open bedrooms with their brothers and their parents? When Daddy stopped drinking, calm had descended between her parents like manna from above. But Bill had reverted to his strangeness. Tension once again filled the air.

Though the tension crackled between Bill and Mother now, Bill sided against Daddy whenever he could, complaining of his past disgusting drunkenness and of how Daddy had abused him when in that state. Kay had never seen or heard it, and how could she not have when even the softest noises echoed down the rooms? When she stuck up for Daddy, Bill jeered that everyone knew he was her favorite. She was taken aback by Bill's viciousness, though she knew it was true. Mother, with her strict rules about decorum and appearance, in contrast with Daddy and his gentle ways, his jaunty whistling, and telling of stories: The choice was no choice.

What a relief it would be to return to her home with its separate bedrooms off a true hallway—inner doors that could stay closed, that didn't need to be walked through to get somewhere else. She promised herself that her children would be safe and secure, away from the city, with a father who was a provider.

Bill reached into the medicine cabinet for aspirin, knocking over Helen's Thorazine. It sounded like a boulder falling off a cliff. Why was no pill available for him? Why were there two family members with these types of illnesses in what was not a large family? Make that three: His father's drunkenness was the bad thread woven into the fabric of the family. It should have been snapped, the way his mother snapped an errant thread as she ran her sewing machine.

Nausea overwhelmed him, and he eased himself down to the bed. What would it be like to have a sofa? They'd never had one. Only enough space for the two dusty armchairs in the front room and, when needed, two or three dining chairs straddling the border of that room and the next. The stacks of books and newspapers weren't noticed any longer; when more got added to a pile and it started to topple, the brittle newspapers were thrown out. Trivial thoughts ran through his brain as his body recalled the shocks to his inner core—the pain he couldn't resist, then the limpness. He couldn't remember what he'd been doing before the so-called treatments, only the passion that filled his days and caused him sleepless hours, joyous feelings he never wanted to end. Now he worked until depression hit, black fog causing his mind to blank, his body to curl inward. Once Beryl returned, she would be his helpmeet, and he wouldn't have to leave the house again.

WHEN her poem was included in a national publication, Helen became insufferable again. Her local successes—poetry in literary reviews, paintings in art shows on campus—hadn't aroused Bill's ire. She hadn't told anyone she'd submitted, or even written, this poem with its echoes of a personal crucifixion, until she produced the book with a flourish.

"I'm surprised they accepted it due to its religiosity," Bill commented after reading the poem. "I wouldn't have thought that was fashionable."

"I'm sure they saw the existential nature behind it." Helen lit a cigarette and blew smoke through the screen door.

Bill maneuvered around her and her smoke to leave the house. The door banged behind him, and he blinked at the sun. He retreated to the shed he'd built at the back of the property, snug against the new wooden fence the neighbor behind them had erected. Mother had prevailed, and he'd removed his belongings from the other side of the house, now rented to strangers. His work was in the shed, safe from prying eyes, from those who'd try to steal his ideas. He kept the key to its padlock on his person at all times.

Back in the U.S. and staying with a friend of Helen's, Beryl was looking for an apartment for them. Once it was found, Father Kelly would marry them in an intimate ceremony and they'd move into their new home immediately, forgoing a honeymoon. Bill had no desire—or money—for a journey to a holiday spot. He panicked when he had to leave the house. After her transatlantic treks, Beryl said she'd done enough traveling anyway.

The electric light buzzed as he flipped the switch inside the workroom door. He contemplated the unfinished painting on the easel. It was time to get serious. He had his subject: a political one. Perhaps he couldn't get elected, but he could effect change or poke at corruption in other ways. Using the political regionalism of Thomas Hart Benton as inspiration, he decided to expand his theme into oils. Tulane University, bigger and more prestigious than the university Helen attended, was interested in his work for an upcoming exhibit about Storyville, the red-light district of late nineteenth- and early twentieth-century New Orleans. While visiting their library to access the documents and photographs for his models, he'd told the curator about his project. The man had agreed to take a look after it was completed.

Bill turned his gaze to his latest completed model. The bisected windows rising up in a graceful column from the ground floor to the fourth floor were what had drawn him to the original brick building. As he looked at its entrance, the white steps leading to a rounded dark doorway, he felt himself shrinking.

18

THE PROFESSIONAL PHOTOGRAPHS of my parents' wedding in February of 1961 are in black and white; I possess a few in color, pasted into a family album. In some photos, Bill, as an usher, is at the end of the line of groomsmen. He's tall, thin, awkward—his shoulders rounded as if he's aware of his height. My grandmother smiles more than I ever saw her do in person. My grandfather, holding a champagne glass, looks uncomfortable in a photo of the toast; he looks happy in others.

Grandpa Toye's alcoholism had cost him many jobs. After he stopped drinking, or at least from the time of my awareness until shortly before his death, he worked as a night watchman at an apartment building. Grandma Toye worked from their home as a seamstress, her machine seeming to permanently hold some type of fabric. In the corner of the dining room closest to the kitchen, she sat behind the machine, its whirring abruptly silenced when she noticed our entrance through the side door. In my memory she's always working in dim light, caught in the crosshairs of filtered sunshine.

When my mother spoke of her experience of air-raid drills, it may have been in response to my fear during school fire drills. Hearing the alarm shriek, being led into a quiet, straight line with my classmates, I was petrified, my legs barely able to move. Standing in the concrete schoolyard, even knowing nothing was ablaze, I didn't feel calmer. I felt like an open target, though that was years before school shootings. In second grade, a firefighter spoke to our class. He gave us supposedly age-appropriate literature with an illustration of a ladder in front of a child at a second-story window, red flames behind his head. I lay in bed at night, wondering how I'd be able to feel if my door was hot to the touch; break my bedroom window; warn my family; and stop, drop, and roll—all at the same time.

Security was my mother's favorite catchword when it came to relationships; from the time I had my first boyfriend in high school, she championed the concept. She never said it was more important than love, she never mentioned love, but I got the message—not that I agreed. It was one of those things she did insidiously, whether she was fully conscious of it or not. It took me some time to realize she must have felt this way about security because she felt she had none growing up.

An example of her craftiness comes to mind: My mother would say my dad was friendly to all, from blue-collar workers to the company president. I'd believed that; I'd seen him chatting with the parking-lot attendants and janitorial staff when he'd take my brothers and me to his office on the weekends, saying he had to pick up some papers—leaving us free to roam through the empty, echoing rooms, to spin on the conference-room chairs while he couldn't help himself and started working at his desk. I'd never met the company president, so I believed Mama, though I should have been able to see for myself from the look he'd get on his face when the man's name came up that Daddy didn't like him. It took my husband's hearing this story, secondhand from me, several years after Daddy's death, to tell me it wasn't true.

"Wasn't true?"

"No, your dad didn't care to socialize with the 'upper class,' and he didn't do it. He ignored them. Your mom thought if she said it enough, it would be true."

His statement hit me with the force of truth. In my stunned silence I wondered what else I'd believed all these years that wasn't true.

19

Other Rooms

"**H**ERE'S OUR ARTIST." The head librarian introduced the visiting professor to Bill. "Professor Stein was complimenting your model of Lulu White's, as well as the Broadway Cabaret." He gestured behind them.

Professor Stein shook Bill's hand. "The Cabaret is an interesting choice. We all know the infamous Mahogany Hall, of course, but why the Cabaret?" The men walked to the models.

"It is an ugly building—flat roof, nothing to distinguish it from any other, though the scrolling is detailed and unusual," Bill said as he ran his finger along the top. "It's important because it was owned by the also-infamous, though lesser-known, Billy Struve, the so-called Billy News; he was a reporter. He quit journalism and became the right-hand man of the so-called mayor of Storyville, Tom Anderson, and compiled the Blue Book for him. I'm sure you've seen a copy of it in this exhibit." Bill gestured toward the glass cases, and Professor Stein nodded. "I find Struve the more fascinating figure, though he's largely forgotten. Not only did he write the Storyville guidebooks—I'm sure he did the research too." He lifted a corner of his mouth in a knowing smile, and the other men chuckled. "When Anderson returned to his oil business, then 'got' religion," Bill said, "Struve remained involved in the daily operations of Anderson's Astoria Club, where the so-called underworld met for pay-offs. He stayed in the shadows, and it can be argued had the better life."

Bill took a breath. "There are descendants who were tied up in the work he was doing who are still alive." The two men looked at each other, and Bill wondered if they believed his last statement. *It could be true.*

"Fascinating," said Professor Stein. "It's been a pleasure talking to you." They shook hands all around.

As the two men left the exhibit room, Bill saw another figure turning away—perhaps someone who'd been there the whole time, eavesdropping, noting his last sentence in particular.

He looked around for Beryl and spotted her chatting earnestly with a group of well-dressed older women. She faced him, and he signaled that he needed her. She stepped away from the group, and the circle of women closed, absorbing the space she'd vacated.

"Did you see that man? The one who slunk away? He passed you as he left."

Beryl clutched the sleeve of Bill's only summer suit. "Who do you think he was? He left very quickly." Her brown eyes grew bigger, darker. "Should I follow him?"

"That would be dangerous. But we'll be on alert. The city must've heard about my paintings and sent one of their henchmen."

"I should've stayed home to guard them. Let's go."

They made their abrupt goodbyes, leaving curious looks they didn't see in their wake. A short walk to St. Charles Avenue took them to the streetcar line that traveled a straight path to their apartment building.

Beryl paced up and down the carpeted hallway. Her face wore that brooding expression she got right before she took to bed with a panic attack. Bill sought to soothe her. "Please don't worry, dear. I'll come up with something."

She turned to him. "We can't pay the rent this month. We have no income coming in. What do you suggest?" The question was brusque, but he didn't take it personally.

"Sales at the exhibit will certainly be high." He folded his arms and smiled at her.

She dropped into the chair that sat in the entryway as if it were looking at the front door, waiting for someone else besides the two who lived here to arrive. "Will they?" she said softly. "I'm not so sure. Granted, Hurricane Camille did not hurt New Orleans, but no one's focus will be on art yet."

"*Au contraire*—the residents will be so relieved the city was spared, they will flock to the show. There couldn't be a better time for 'Complacency is Alive and Well in New Orleans,'" Bill said with a flourish of his arm.

"No," Beryl stood up decisively. "We need to do something."

"You can see the mutilation, Officer." Bill pointed out the gaping holes in the paintings, all forty-four bearing at least one cavity.

"But, sir, why would anyone take the time to damage the paintings instead of carrying them away?" Perplexed, the policeman looked up from his scrutiny.

"With all due respect, that's not my area of concern, but yours." Bill swept his arm around the room that he used for his studio, the early-September sun passing through the sheer white curtains covering the two guillotine windows. "Perhaps they didn't have time to take all of them; perhaps the thieves were too few and my paintings too many." He looked as if he were quickly calculating. "Six are missing. Most of these that are damaged are of a highly sensitive political nature. Are you familiar with the artist Thomas Hart Benton?"

The other man shook his head.

"He—I won't say sneaked—he incorporated figures such as a political-machine boss and even the Ku Klux Klan into his historical murals, and that was in Indiana. I've done the same in my paintings in regard to New Orleans, and those are the very objects that have been cut from my works."

"Well, I can see that some are slashed and that makes sense, but why someone would take the time to bore holes through the canvases—"

The officer's partner darkened the doorway. "The security guard at the gate saw nothing, said he must've been distracted by a car accident down the block."

"Our front door was locked when we left home this morning," Bill offered.

"Looks like the lock was picked," the second officer said. "And that they left through the back door. Where's your wife now, Mr. Toye?"

"With my parents—my father is not well and she's helping my mother. I came home to do some mounting. My show opens in ten days," he said with a note of panic in his otherwise steady voice.

"I'm sorry to hear that," the first officer said, scribbling on his pad of paper. "How much are your paintings worth?"

Again, Bill looked as if he were quickly calculating. "The six that were taken are the most controversial; the thieves must've known that. They could've sold for $1,000 apiece. The others, the ones here," he gestured toward the damaged paintings, "are probably worth half as much." Bill sat on the stool by his easel and put his head in his hands. "I'm ruined."

"You have insurance, don't you?" the officer asked. Bill nodded. "Here's your copy of the report. Good day, Mr. Toye."

Bɪʟʟ had left Beryl in a dimly lit Royal Street gold shop, whispered in her ear as she talked to the man behind the counter that he was going to the Jackson Square gallery and wouldn't be long. She nodded, deep in thought, though he didn't know what she was contemplating.

Mrs. Marshall came forward to clasp Bill's hand. "I am sorry for your paintings. I was looking forward to hosting your exhibition."

Bill had wandered around the gallery before Mrs. Marshall had emerged from her office in the back, imagining his work displayed alongside Dureau and Rockmore, darlings of the insider art world. "Ma'am, the artist here," he pointed toward the far wall. "What can you tell me about her?"

"Untaught, started late in life, lives on a plantation in Natchitoches."

Bill had gleaned those facts from his readings; what he wanted to know was what drew people to her creations. "Do you like her work?" He tried not to be blunt but knew of no other way to ask. "It's quite primitive."

"Oh, very much so." She stopped to look at him inquisitively, and Bill wasn't sure which of his sentences she'd answered. "All art is personal, isn't it, but look here." She strode to the wall displaying the Hunter art. "It's direct. It's historical"—she turned to smile at him—"as was your unfortunate work." She turned back to the paintings. "Authenticity can be very appealing. The leftover boards she paints upon, the subjects she depicts—they're more than a glimpse into her world. They tell stories." She pointed at four different pieces: "You can almost see each day of the week: the backbreaking monotony of wash day and cotton picking, drunken violence on a Saturday night, Sunday churchgoers. They're starting to sell too," she added with an impish smile.

Bill had heard enough. He turned away from the wall. "Thank you for all you've done. It will be my one eternal regret that I was not able to show in your illustrious gallery."

With a slightly amused smile, Mrs. Marshall took his hand. "Good luck to you."

Bill strolled down Pirates Alley back to Royal. It seemed like it was always September, and September felt too much like August. The bell tinkled as he opened the door to Mr. Guggenheimer's store.

Beryl was slipping a wrapped package into her purse, expressing her thanks to the shop owner. "I'll be in touch." She gave him a small wave before turning away from the counter.

Mr. Guggenheimer looked up and over the tops of his glasses as he locked the clear case in front of him. "My pleasure—I hope to see you soon."

Beryl gave Bill a radiant smile as he held the door open for her. "What did you buy? You know we can't afford anything in there."

"Shush. I bought nothing. Mr. Guggenheimer gave me a small piece of gold. I told him I was interested in making jewelry. He wants to see what I can do."

Bill looked at her in bewilderment as they walked to Canal Street to catch the streetcar. "How will you do that?"

"Trust me. I know what I'm doing."

On the streetcar Bill sat next to the open window to spare Beryl's hair. "By the way," Beryl said, "I spoke to your parents. Well, to your mother." Each phrase arrived with a hesitant, gleeful expectation. "She's agreed to let us rent the other half of their house."

"Alleluia." Bill leaned against the window in relief. "You are a miracle worker."

"I know." She patted his hand and looked ahead, her smile one of smugness and superiority. "With Helen gone, there should be no conflicts."

Bill thought how lucky he was to have such a partner. "Peace will reign over the days of our lives." He too acquired a smile of self-satisfaction.

HELEN had been accepted into Kent State's graduate school on the strength of her poems and her coursework in Loyola University's evening division. Unlike most of the coeds, she worked during the day and could only take night classes. A year later, she was on the editorial board for Kent State's literary magazine *The Human Issue*. In partial deference to the campus never being the same again after the events of May 4, 1970, they'd changed the journal's title and format. Her time in Ohio was not long; she left after two semesters. Her roommate found her curled in a blanket, unable to get out of bed, convinced she'd been shot and that she was bleeding on the grass of the commons.

20

AN ARTICLE TITLED "Exhibit Based on Storyville" in the May 9, 1968, *Times-Picayune* reports that a highlight of the exhibit was William Toye's model of Mahogany Hall and the adjoining Broadway Saloon, on public view for the first time. The curator of the Tulane Archive of New Orleans Jazz, Richard B. Allen, is quoted as saying the highly detailed scale model is a correct representation, "down to the accurate number of bricks." In addition to this description of Bill's models, nine of his oil paintings are briefly described in the article.

In August of 1969, Hurricane Camille hit the Gulf Coast area, largely sparing New Orleans, though the city hunkered down for its threat. On September 3, 1969, a *Times-Picayune* headline reads, "44 Paintings Are Destroyed: 6 Others Stolen from Artist's Apartment." Naomi Marshall, founder of the Downtown Gallery, announced via the September 7, 1969, newspaper that Bill's exhibit was canceled. The news item reiterated the account from the earlier article of the thefts and vandalism perpetrated on the paintings that were to be in the exhibit. After writing this part of Bill's story, I had lunch at Madewood Plantation in connection with a ranger-led boat tour out of Thibodaux in late April of 2016. On our way into the dining room, I stopped at a portrait of Naomi Marshall on the wall, recognizing her name from my research. Then and there, I discovered she was a former owner of the plantation home. Her son greeted us at lunch. Marshall's obituary describes her as a patron of the arts who launched the careers of many Louisiana artists, "being among the first to exhibit their works in her galleries."[8] If my uncle had trusted his original work and kept to a licit path, Marshall might have been as influential on a potential legitimate career for him as she'd been for such multitalented artists as Noel Rockmore and George Dureau.

My mother never mentioned the theft or the destruction of Bill's paintings; if she had, she likely would've said it was another example of his bad luck. The instance she usually cited was of the floats he'd designed and overseen the construction of for a Mardi Gras parade in Mobile, Alabama. On their way out of New Orleans, bad weather popped up on the highway, and the floats were damaged beyond repair before they'd even arrived. While reading of incidents such as the vandalism of his paintings, though I have no evidence of dishonesty or deception, I became skeptical of his "bad luck," thinking some of it had to be of his own making.

Mama told me of Beryl's jewelry-making venture and showed me a design for a ring she'd outlined on a scrap piece of paper. I was either in my late high-school years or home for a visit from college when I went with her to the pick-up location in the Riverbend area, not far from my grandparents' house. We approached a shabby, purple-painted building in a row of similar edifices on a brilliant sunshiny day. A window with black trim looked boarded up, but it opened and a black-felt box was put in Mama's hand. The ring was bright gold and swirled high like soft-serve ice cream. It was much bigger, more ostentatious, than any other ring Mama owned. I don't know if the ring was a gift or if my mother paid for it. While searching *Times-Picayune* archives for Beryl's name, I came across two small claims court cases in the 1980s when she sued gold companies for damages and labor costs.

In the early 2000s, I proofread a memoir Aunt Helen had written. She sent the manuscript to publishers with no success. The work dealt with her mental illness, the dangers she faced during her schizophrenic episodes, and her hospitalizations, told in a poetic, hallucinatory way. I remember reading about her time at Kent State and how hopeful she was about being a part of the university's healing process, only a semester after the Ohio National Guard fatally shot four students during an anti-war rally on campus. She likely hoped for her own healing as well. Instead, her schizophrenia deluded her into believing she was living through horrors she hadn't actually experienced.

21

A Suburban House

THE SCHOOLBAG on her shoulder full of heavy seventh-grade textbooks, Teresa slid open the glass door and walked into the den where Mama was folding clothes. A game show blared from the TV. As usual, her brothers had run ahead and already were changing their khaki school uniforms for shorts and T-shirts. Over the TV, she heard bedroom and bathroom doors banging. "Where's the newspaper?"

Mama dropped the sock she was holding while searching for its mate. "Why? What do you want it for?"

"To read it. Like I do every day." Teresa couldn't help sounding annoyed. "It's usually right here." *And in a messed-up clump, on a corner of the sofa, in a laundry basket, or stuffed into a side of the recliner*, she stopped herself from saying. Mama read the paper at odd moments, folding the pages to an interesting article, leaving crumpled sections wherever she'd been sitting when she got up to answer the phone, finish a chore, or start another one. Teresa didn't read the whole newspaper, but always Ann Landers and Dear Abby, the comics, and sometimes the sports section.

"Oh, Resa, I don't know. I guess it didn't come today."

"Teresa." She emphasized the first syllable; she'd been correcting her family all school year, determined to get rid of the nickname Mama loved. She sat on the couch next to Mama and started folding. "Did you call them?" As soon as she asked, Teresa knew it was the wrong thing to say. Mama's approach to her tasks seemed haphazard, but she immediately called the newspaper office when a paper wasn't delivered.

She knew Daddy would expect the paper to be there waiting for him when he got home from work. Sitting in his chair, at the table or in the den, he'd grumble about the state it was in and complain that sections were missing. Teresa would do her best to retrieve them and put them in some kind of order.

Mama let out a big sigh, almost a screech. "I don't have time for everything. Now could you please leave me alone?" Her voice rose to a whine, and she stomped her foot.

Teresa stopped folding a pair of white socks belonging to one of the boys, picked up her schoolbag, and went to her room. Catching a glimpse of herself in the mirror over the dresser, her long, curly—frizzy—hair, her gold wire-rimmed glasses, and thinking of the braces behind her tightly closed lips, she released the tears that had sprung to her eyes. She hated how easily they did.

After Teresa left the room, Kay sighed, warding off tears of her own. She'd done her crying last night—after Mother had called, after the numbness had worn off, after she'd told Ted what had happened. He'd shaken his head and emitted that exasperated noise he made, air puffing through closed lips, when he didn't know what to say: That was when she'd burst into tears. They hadn't watched the ten o'clock news as they usually did in case any of the kids had wandered from their bedrooms. Thank goodness the neighbors and the parents of her children's friends didn't know her maiden name. It wasn't something they'd remember even if it had been discussed. As soon as one said "I do," maiden surnames became superfluous, were not given a second thought. Kay had taken relish in reminding the storekeepers and cashiers who'd looked at the checks she'd signed and made assumptions about her ethnicity that she wasn't born married. But now the obliviousness about a woman having an identity before marriage was a relief.

She'd spent a restless night and left their bed when she heard the newspaper hit the front walkway. It was still dark outside, and Ted was still sleeping. Why would it bother him? It wasn't his brother.

Afraid to take the rubber band off the paper right away, she'd gone into the kitchen and started the coffee. She took a clean mug from the kitchen counter where she'd set the clean dishes last night. She would've left them in the washer, but she needed the space for the dirty ones from yesterday's breakfast, lunch, and snacks that were in the sink, so there'd be room there for last night's pots, pans, and dinner dishes, which she'd left soaking overnight. Like the laundry, it was a never-ending carousel, but without the chirpy, diverting music.

She'd sat at the table and unrolled the newspaper. Above the fold on page 8—she'd feared it would be front-page news—was a huge headline about Bill's arrest. At the tangible evidence, shock had coursed through her again. Feeling guilty herself, she'd gone to the bedroom to show the paper to Ted.

Ted swiped at the fogged bathroom mirror and combed his wet hair. He thought of his brilliant and crazy brother-in-law, how Bill had designed this house to Ted's specifications without any formal training. His blueprints were perfect, beautiful enough to hang on a wall. He'd taught himself, or it all came naturally—Ted wasn't sure which. He was reminded of his father, who could do complicated mathematics in his head, arriving at the answer without being able to explain how he'd done it. He hoped none of the children would inherit whatever mental illness came from Kay's family. His dad had exhibited some volatility at the end of his life, but that was age-related; he was sure of it.

Humidity escaped into the bedroom as he opened the bathroom door. Kay was back in bed, asleep, her robe over her nightgown. He picked up the newspaper next to her. The situation was worse than he feared. After retrieving his briefcase from under Kay's rumpled clothes on the armchair, he stowed the newspaper inside. He smelled freshly brewed coffee, but he supposed he'd have to make his own toast. When he'd awoken and seen Kay was gone, he'd decided to reverse his usual order of breakfast before shaving and showering. He hadn't felt like talking—still didn't. Ted prided himself on his objectivity, and Kay was too emotional. He'd wake her before he walked out the front door; she had to get the kids ready for school.

Kay's sleepless night had turned into a deep early-morning nap. After Ted had woken her, she'd lain there for a moment not remembering what her vague feeling of unease meant—then its cause came rushing back. The next moment she told herself it would be okay: The kids wouldn't know; the neighbors wouldn't know. She'd visit her parents after the school bus took the kids away, and she'd be back home long before they returned. After today, she'd put all this about Bill out of her mind.

22

ANY NEWSPAPER could've been easily "lost" in our chaotic household of six children, all under the age of thirteen, without my suspecting anything. I grew up hearing my dad complain of not being able to find all the sections of the newspaper, my mother wondering where in the world the scissors could be every time she needed them. When my parents acquired a television with a remote control, the controller was never where it should be, arguments ensued, and Daddy finally tied it down to the arm of his chair.

Mama and I watched *Gone with the Wind* together when it first aired on TV in 1976. Her favorite line from the movie was "Tomorrow is another day"; she quoted it often. Like Scarlett O'Hara, she put aside things she didn't want to face and relied on tomorrow never arriving. But it's no wonder if Mama was as frazzled and sometimes as short-tempered as I remember her being. Less than two years before my uncle's 1974 arrest, my father had surgery for colon cancer, a colostomy, and chemotherapy; he'd gone back to work as soon as possible. Details about Daddy's health were doled out to us children in increments; we only pieced them together as adults, and some things are still unclear.

Like a perpetual puzzle, other elements are still being pieced together. Kevin remembers our mom being upset at this time and discussing Bill's need for a lawyer with our dad, himself an attorney. Ten years old then, Kevin was maybe more alert to clues than the rest of us. I once found him standing on a chair in our parents' bedroom, searching the top shelf of Mama's closet for Christmas presents. Even if Mama was more open than I knew about Bill's first arrest, Kevin remembers nothing else being said in his hearing, whether from his being in the same room or from his listening around the hallway corner. Watergate wasn't the only cover-up happening at the time.

WHEN I was school-age, we children rarely came through the front door of our house. We entered through the back sliding-glass door into the den or through the side door into the garage, which led into the kitchen. The front door opened to the only room without clutter, and Mama kept the accordion doors between the front room (the so-called living room) and the den (our true living room) habitually closed, especially when visitors were expected.

Visitors sat in the front room on the small sofa—*loveseat* we were supposed to call it, my brothers twisting the word into mockery—from which they could see Aunt Helen's landscape paintings of Italy and Ireland. Above the rarely used piano, hanging on the wall, was a colorized portrait of my three brothers and me from when I was four years old. As the oldest, I'd been placed at one end with the boys in front of me, descending in age to Paul, who was ten months old. I remember being uncomfortable during the photoshoot, holding a smile as I sat astride a bench too wide for my short legs. The picture wasn't updated, or removed, after the two youngest were born, though eventually their school pictures were framed and placed on top of the piano. Directly opposite the sofa were the closed doors. The latter was what visitors must've found strange— wondering what was lurking behind them, hearing the lowered TV and giggles and exaggerated whispers. Mama would caution us into silence before she answered the door, first looking out the peephole to see who was waiting on the porch. More often than not, someone was dropping off unexplained papers for Daddy. Mama was expecting the knock or the bell, yet still she looked before opening.

In April of 1976, near the end of my first year of high school, I walked past the kitchen into the den and found Mama sitting in her chair, crying. My siblings, home before I was as my commute was the longest, stood around, looking helpless. The unusual scene caused me to feel as if my heart had climbed into my throat.

"Oh, Resa," my mother may have said through tears. Her emotions easily rose to the surface. "Grandpa Toye is worse." Cancer from his esophagus had been removed, and he was in the hospital recuperating.

The use of the nickname would've niggled, but I wouldn't have corrected her then. Fear coursed through my body. Except for my paternal grandfather's death when I was seven, no one in my family had died, and I didn't know how to react. I stood in front of Mama, books in my arms, frozen. "I thought he was getting better." My voice sounded small. I hadn't known what it would say, if anything.

"He fell out of bed. He's coughing up blood. I'm not sure what happened." The telephone rang, startling my stomach. "That's Helen." Mama ran to the phone on the kitchen wall, lifted the receiver, and pulled it into Daddy's study as she routinely did when she took a call with us children around. The door to the study closed on the long white cord, pinching and flattening one of its coils.

In my bedroom, still feeling panicky, I pulled from my old ballerina-less jewelry box the crystal rosary Grandma Rose, my paternal grandmother, had given me the previous year for confirmation and started praying.

23

Orchestrating

"THIS TOWN has never seen the likes of our company before. It will be an unqualified success." Without calling first, to avoid being rebuffed, Bill had shown up at the newspaper office and asked to see the "amusements" editor. He'd been vetted enough, he presumed, to be ushered to the man's cubicle and offered a chair.

"There's the Symphony," the other man said.

Bill did his best not to scoff, reminding himself this was his one big chance at advertising his next venture. "Our performances will be in the summer to avoid any conflicts with them, as well as to give music-loving citizens a balm during our sweltering temperatures." He paused to dab at his forehead. "It will be an intimate experience. The Civic Theater and *The Pirates of Penzance* are perfect for a 30-piece chamber orchestra to introduce themselves to our city. I will conduct and serve as stage director and set designer. I've been trained by Alexander Hilsberg and Lothar Wallerstein." Though he'd merely sat in on performances of the local orchestra when it was guest-conducted by Hilsberg and worked on the sets for only one Wallerstein locally produced opera, both men were dead and could not be reached for confirmation. "My roots also extend into these fields."

The editor twisted his chair, side to side and back again. "Your roots?"

"The Toye name is well known in classical music, especially Sir Geoffrey." Bill ticked off each item on a different finger: "Managing director of the Royal Opera House, principal conductor of the D'Oyly Carte, producer of the original film version of *The Mikado*." He lowered his hand. "We'll be putting on *The Mikado* at a later date. Sir Geoffrey also rewrote the overture to *Ruddigore*." Damn the man; he was not writing any of this down. "His brother, Francis Toye, was the music critic for the *Times of*

London and has written many books on music, including one on Gilbert and Sullivan. I know them all."

"Don't forget Jennifer Toye, dear," said Beryl. She'd insisted on standing, and he could feel her fingers grazing his back as her hands rested on the top of the chair.

"Ah, yes, thank you, my dear; Jennifer Toye sang with the D'Oyly Carte and made several recordings with the company." He gestured toward Beryl. "Besides reminding me of such things, my wife is handling our public relations. I've enlisted the services of choral director Larry Wyatt, and singers Nancy Assaf and Anthony Laciura. Father McNaspy is my adviser." The man was still not taking notes. "He's in the Music Department at Loyola, as I'm sure you know. Here's my press release, as well as some photographs. I thought it best to deliver them in person."

Whether the editor believed Bill's claims or recognized Bill's name from his arrest two years prior, Bill didn't know; but a notice about his orchestra appeared in Frank Gagnard's "On the Scene" column a short time later. It was the lead, the headline trumpeting "Operettas to Introduce Group," and accompanied by one of the photographs. Nancy, Larry, and Anthony sat around the table that held his stage set model for *The Pirates of Penzance*, while he and Beryl stood next to each other. Identified only as Mrs. Toye, Beryl looked fetching, her dark hair casting a shadow across her features as she looked downward, her thin arm supporting her as she leaned over the scrim. Bill thought being called a "music enthusiast" made him sound dilettantish, but otherwise he couldn't complain. The journalist had even cited Bill's familial credentials. Bill cut out the article, excising the notice directly below it of the community college's driver-education course.

24

Locked Houses

"I'M GOING TO THAT NEW DISCO with Brian tonight," Teresa informed her mother after an early Saturday dinner of leftovers.

"Where is it?"

"The Civic, somewhere downtown. Brian knows."

"I know it. Be careful. I don't know how that neighborhood is any longer."

"It's fine." Ted was trying to be reassuring, Kay knew, but all she could hear was his contradicting her, the intimation that he knew more than she did. In this case he did, since his office was not far from the Civic.

"Be sure to lock up when you get home," Kay said as Teresa walked down the hallway to her bedroom.

"I wonder what your brother thinks of the Civic being turned into a disco. Perhaps he welcomes the transformation of the site of another of his failures."

Ted had echoed Kay's thoughts, but she was still feeling contrary. "It isn't his fault an audience didn't show up. He has such bad luck."

BILL cracked open the front door, reached his hand around its edge, lifted the lid of the mailbox, and retrieved the contents. Shuffling through what looked like bills, his eyes were drawn to an envelope without a stamp and with familiar handwriting. He tore it open. How ridiculous for Helen to write him when she lived right next door in the same house. He glanced at it and threw it aside, more excuses why she couldn't lend him any money: Mother's medical bills, the expenses of running the house. What rubbish! He had to have the car repaired.

"CALL the police!" Bill shouted to a man in front of the church heading toward the streetcar stop.

As Bill pulled out his handkerchief to wipe his face, the man jumped back. "What happened?"

Bill transferred the handkerchief to his arm and quickly removed it to show him a spot of blood upon the whiteness of the cloth. "I was grabbed by two thugs. They couldn't have been more than sixteen. They cut me on my arm with—I don't know what. I fell and threw them my wallet. They took all my cash, a twenty-dollar bill, and then fled. How this could happen in the middle of the day is inconceivable!"

"Yeah, okay." The man took Bill's elbow and guided him inside the church. He left him in the cool, dim lobby while he went to the rectory to find a telephone, and a priest.

WHILE Helen was showing her paintings at a new arts and crafts fair, Kay sat with Mother. Kay had gone to church in the morning, fed her family—excluding her two oldest, now at out-of-state universities—their big Sunday meal, still every week at noon, then slipped away. It was quiet at Mother's house but not peaceful, at least not in Kay's head. She was worried about Teresa, who had a new boyfriend—inevitable, Kay knew, but not at all the type she'd envisioned for her sensible oldest. Kay had met him when they'd come in for Mardi Gras, and she could tell it was all happening too fast. Now this immediate worry: Mother, always in control and controlling, wondering where she'd left her glasses when they were on her nose; starting to work on a client's dress, then stopping in confusion. She'd never felt sorry for Mother before, but it was impossible not to now. Sitting in the front room she no longer felt comfortable in, Kay looked at her idle mother in the chair opposite her, and tears came to her eyes. Helen's cat pounced on the arm of Kay's chair, and whether it sensed she needed comfort or felt Kay was intruding, she didn't care. All she felt was irritation. She pushed the cat off and felt a little bit better.

ANOTHER invention, another patent pending: The drawings and painting of his internal combustion turbine sat in the shed—the patent approved years ago, though the engine was never developed; it'd be different with this one, Bill thought. Already he had one customer who had flood-proofed his home with the help of Waterlock Flood Control Systems and, with the right publicity, there'd be more. Damn Helen for saying the name sounded witchlike and that his company would be cursed. The crazy woman believed in numerology too. He knew he shouldn't be upset by her silliness, but she knew how to unnerve him.

The money from the first (and only) customer had gone into advertising and the care of his and Beryl's beloved cats. The veterinarian likely wouldn't take another painting as payment, though the oil he'd received was displayed prominently in his waiting room, a loving portrait of Pretty Sing curled up on an inside window ledge. Parting with it hadn't been difficult for Bill; he could easily paint another with the new supplies he'd bought with the last of the money.

The mail brought a request for more information from someone who'd seen the local news feature about his company, even though it had aired six months earlier. The man wrote that his house had been severely flooded on two occasions and asked if Bill could please get in touch about his anti-flood system. Bill and Beryl's phone had been disconnected so he'd have to call from Mother's, or he could write the man back. He'd ask Beryl to do it; lately, she had more energy than he did.

25

Aᴘᴛᴇʀ Aᴜɴᴛ Hᴇʟᴇɴ's ᴅᴇᴀᴛʜ, I discovered in a small wooden box a letter she'd written to her brother Bill about there being no money for his car repair. Tom and I had cleared out her nursing-home room and brought most of her belongings to our house for me to sort. Thinking my mother would want to see them, I gave her the box and its contents; there were a few other items in the box besides the letter. I wondered why my aunt had the letter in her possession. Perhaps it wasn't given to Bill—maybe they talked instead; perhaps he sent it back to her in a fit of pique. Her keeping it is intriguing. After Mama's death, when I went to clean her house one last time, after almost everything had been cleared away, I spotted the box under her dresser. The letter was no longer inside. Perhaps my mother threw it away as a sign of discord she wanted to elim-inate. It was as if my aunt sent the letter to me, wanting it to be seen, and my mother threw it out, hoping it wouldn't be. Though I always knew my mother and her sister to get along, they'd always been opposites.

A police report filed under "Assaults" in the *Times-Picayune* of May 22, 1981, describes an incident at the intersection of Oak and South Carrollton at "about 12:45 p.m. Sunday." It gives Bill's age as forty-nine and says that after being cut on the arm with an unknown type of weapon, he fell and threw his wallet to the teens, "from which they took $20." My mother never mentioned this incident to me; if she'd known of it, it would've scared her. She would have added it to her mental list of reasons not to go to the city. When she was a young woman, before she married, she worked as a receptionist for an insurance company. One day a man with a gun came into the office. She and others who worked there were made to lie on the floor as the man stole money from wallets and purses.

During a visit to Uncle Bill at his nursing home, my brother Paul was given a painting of Bill's patented engine. When I saw the painting and heard the word "engine," I thought of a train, the front of it confronting the viewer face-on, ready to mow one down, with no time to get out of its way.

In more recent years, after Aunt Helen's death, a friend told me a painting of a cat she thought was by Helen hangs on the wall of her veterinarian's office; she figured it was given in lieu of payment. That sounded more like my uncle's style. A few years later I met a woman who worked at that same veterinarian's office and had done so for years. She confirmed that it was Bill's painting and that he and Beryl owed her boss more than paintings could ever repay. Her boss, the veterinarian, sounded like a patient, kind man. I'm sure he had to put up with more than she felt comfortable telling me. Later I found in "Court Records: Judgments," the *Times-Picayune* of December 20, 1985, "Maple Small Animal Clinic vs William Toye; $419."

26

Losses

THE FUNERAL MASS for Grandma Toye was over, but Uncle Bill was only arriving now. Carrying Rhea, my infant daughter, I squinted into the winter sunshine to see him standing on the sidewalk in front of the church. He made his way up the church steps, perspiring in the winter sun as if he'd been jogging. Breathing heavily, he looked nervous, every action a great effort. It was painful to watch, and though I anticipated his greeting me with his usual "Baby Doll," I couldn't look him in the eyes. I needn't have worried; he didn't see me.

Mama had said Uncle Bill likely wouldn't attend the funeral due to an emotionally scarring childhood experience. When he was very young, he'd been forced to approach the open casket of a distant relative and kiss her on her cold, firm, unyielding cheek. It was the reason Mama didn't make any of us children go to funerals or wakes. My siblings had attended Grandma Toye's funeral, and Daddy had left to take them home before heading to work. I wondered if Uncle Bill's funeral-phobia or his agoraphobia had taken precedence today, or if it was one and the same.

After exchanging a few words with Mama, Aunt Beryl and Uncle Bill left to take the short walk to the house. Mama turned to talk to Aunt Helen and the parish priest. Helen had been the reader during Mass, and I marveled at her faith, incongruous in one who gave the impression of being radical. I wondered if it was a habit Aunt Helen found hard to break—like my tendency to suck on the end of my hair, which I stopped doing when I insisted on no longer being called Resa. The women finished their conversation with the priest, and we three generations left Carrollton Avenue and walked down Plum Street.

The last time I'd been in the house, Rhea was one month old. Now, five months later, the baby's great-grandmother was dead. During the visit, I'd dutifully leaned over the hospital bed to show her to my grandmother.

Aunt Helen had crooned, "Look, Mother, your first great-grandchild. Can you believe little Teresa has a baby?" Grandma Toye's eyes were open and seemed focused, and Mama snapped a photo for posterity's sake. After the photograph was developed, I saw that the old woman's eyes were blank and unseeing, and I remembered that not once had they strayed to me, or to Mama.

By the time we'd walked the two blocks from the church to the house, Bill and Beryl had disappeared into their side, and I wondered why he'd bothered leaving in the first place. I still didn't know what their side of the house looked like; I still wasn't sure how they entered and exited it. Their front door seemed to exist in a state of nonuse. If their half had a side door, I'd never seen it. If it did exist, it was behind the padlocked gate in front of the skinny alleyway next to the neighbor's house. A view of their back door was blocked by the canopies of tall trees on both sides of a fence that split the back area into two. As a child I'd stood on one of the chairs on my grandparents' side trying to see over the fence. I wasn't brave enough to stand on the table, and whatever I hoped to see eluded me.

A few of Aunt Helen's friends were in the house. They'd been at the funeral; I'd spotted them in the pews several rows behind the family—her best friends, two poets and two men, one of whom was Mama's favorite. He was the most "normal," Mama would say, meaning not eccentric like the others, whatever those words meant to her. After her last hospital stay, the two men had helped move Grandma Toye into the house and into the bed set up in the dining room; Mama had witnessed the process and was eternally grateful to them. The rest of Helen's friends made their way over to the house in dribs and drabs. As a rule, they had no money and were always ready for a party, especially when Helen was making Black Russians. They teased Mama about living in the suburbs to her innocent incomprehension about what could possibly be wrong with that.

I'd admired Aunt Helen's fortitude while she was Grandma Toye's primary caregiver. She'd kept her job since her boss allowed her to work from home. After business hours, he'd picked up the pages she'd typed for him, asked after her mother, and left her more work. Before this last steady occupation, she'd held down various jobs in succession while dealing with her own illnesses, including schizophrenia—episodes Mama had told me were "nervous breakdowns." Through her struggles, Helen must have acquired not only patience, but the serenity that accompanies it when it's real.

BERYL put a payment down for a corner lot on Annunciation Street. In the alleyway that would exist between the neighboring house and the house she and Bill would build, she'd grow banana trees. She envisioned their dream home: the bottom floor for the living areas; a top floor for the bedroom, Bill's studio, and a workroom for her jewelry-making; their ten cats would live everywhere. She planned dark blinds for the windows. The front door would be solid with no aperture.

ALMOST seven years after his mother's funeral, Uncle Bill was well enough to conduct an orchestra for a performance at the New Orleans Museum of Art. Feeling like a poor relation, which I was now, I borrowed a long dress from my brother's wife for the event. It didn't zip up the whole way, but my long hair concealed the exposed area. Next to Mama, I walked up the wide steps of NOMA in my old platform shoes unearthed from my parents' attic. The bottom of the dress covered the outdated wedges, thank goodness, as there'd been no shoes to borrow, my feet being smaller than those of anyone I knew. Mama wore a beaded two-piece outfit she'd bought for one of Daddy's work galas, and her fancy flats peeked out below the hem of the skirt.

Floor-length, white curtains, lit with purple spotlights and draped to create enticing alcoves, had been added to the walls for the annual Odyssey Ball. A tuxedoed server handed us flutes of champagne. Voices rose in anticipation; glasses clinked. I wondered how much the philanthropists, dressed in black tie and glittery dresses, had paid in order to be seen. I picked up a floorplan and looked for the room Uncle Bill's orchestra was in. As one of the entertainers, he'd received complimentary tickets to the fundraiser and given them to Mama. He was on the second floor, in the Impressionists room.

We walked up the white marble staircase, the centerpiece of the museum, reminiscent of the one Cinderella fled down. If I lost a shoe when I left, it would fit only me, but I wouldn't claim it. Strains of classical music wafted toward us. Bill stood in front of his orchestra, set up on a raised platform for their stage, in front of a Degas. He turned slightly toward the several people making up his audience, and a flicker in his face indicated he'd spotted us as we slid into a row of empty chairs near the back. The name of his band of men was emblazoned across the main podium, a la *The Lawrence Welk Show*, which Mama used to watch faithfully.

"Rhapsody in Blue" ended. Uncle Bill put down his baton and walked toward us. With smiles—Mama's wide and proud, mine tentative—we stood to greet him. He pulled out a handkerchief from his inner jacket pocket and wiped his brow. He gestured to the coffee station in the corner, and we followed him there. Detesting coffee, and seemingly the only person in New Orleans who did, I looked around for another glass of champagne. Magically, a server appeared with a tray.

"Baby Doll, you're all grown up."

He and Aunt Beryl had received invitations to all the major family celebrations: high school graduations, my wedding. We knew they'd never leave their house to attend, yet Mama sent the invitations anyway, considering them indicators of life moving on. Of course no announcement was issued for my divorce, almost a year ago now, and I wondered if Mama had informed them of it, as certainly she must have told them of the birth of my son Mage five years before. I hadn't seen Uncle Bill since the day of Grandma Toye's funeral, and though he seemed basically okay this evening, he was sweating in the chilly air-conditioned venue, furtively looking around as if he'd done something wrong, or as if he suspected someone was lying in wait for him.

27

Newspaper records show that the house at 8208-10 Plum St. was transferred from my mother "and others to Beryl and William J. Toye" for $75,000. At the time it didn't occur to me to wonder how much he'd have to pay his siblings, much less where the money might have come from. I did know the agreement was for Helen to continue to live on "her" side rent-free. "It's only fair," Mama said; "she's the one who took care of your grandmother during her decline until her death." I'd bet anything my dad drew up an airtight agreement stipulating the terms. Despite their purchase of the family home, Bill and Beryl bought a lot on Annunciation Street a few months later. Six months after that a "single, two-story brick dwelling" built there was up for auction.

A few months after my university graduation in the spring of 1983, I returned to New Orleans for good, eventually renting half of a drafty double-shotgun house in the Mid-City area for my family of three. On a sweltering late-September afternoon, Rhea, who was a year old, and I took a drive with my mother to the Plum Street home. I felt carsick, and when we arrived at the house, I quickly opened the car door and vomited into some weeds at the side of the fence. At that moment I knew I was pregnant. My brain was in a haze as I waited for Mama to accomplish the reason for her visit, likely something about the house transfer. I don't remember seeing Uncle Bill. He wasn't inside Aunt Helen's half of the house, and I don't think Mama went into his side. She seemed in a hurry, and I now wonder if Bill was being difficult about the transfer. Her haste wouldn't have struck me as unusual. We kids grew up with her telling us to keep up with her pace.

The encounter at the NOMA fundraiser may have been the last time I saw my uncle in person. Beryl wasn't there. Months after I write the above section about the gala, looking for confirmation of the year, I finally find a *Times-Picayune* article about an Odyssey Ball that sounds like the one I attended.[9] I puzzle over the orchestra being called the Jan

Toye Orchestra; I have no memory of that name being used. I don't remember the room the ensemble played in, so I placed them with the Impressionists, a nod to Bill's possible forgery of Monet, as well as to Degas's connection to New Orleans. Bill told the *Garden & Gun* writer he'd conducted an orchestra of sixty-eight. If he's speaking of this time, he exaggerated. There were about fifteen in the orchestra; the men sat in at least three rows.

After telling one of Helen's best friends I was writing about my family, she shared that when there was a strike at the symphony in 1987, Bill filled in as conductor. How wonderful, the friend said, that they knew they always had someone brilliant like him standing by. And someone willing to be a strikebreaker, though she didn't say that. She did go on to say that she'd never forget sitting in the audience—after reading Bill's biography in the program before the performance started—turning to Helen to exclaim, "I didn't know Bill performed in Covent Garden," and Helen rolling her eyes and responding, "Neither did I." The strikebreaking symphony he conducted could have consisted of sixty-eight musicians, though maybe less with a strike going on.

28

Moving House

Not even a year since the couple had bought the property on Annunciation and the sheriff had foreclosed. Annunciation, ha! Helen thought. The annunciation of shattered hopes and dreams, once again—out of their depth, out of their minds.

Lawsuits followed one after the other, from the end of that year through the end of the next. Ted sent a lawyer friend to help Bill for the first case, as the disputed amount was over $7,000, but Kay said he could do no more, and neither could any other lawyer: It was the *raison d'être* for small claims court. The bills from Acme Lock and the animal clinic couldn't be paid, but their services were vital, Bill thought, especially as the neighborhood deteriorated and their cherished cats multiplied.

They'd deferred the bills for the gold the longest, paying enough to be able to buy more, as Beryl's venture had been the most profitable of any they'd attempted. Her designs were lovely. She had let Kay choose one to thank her for past kindnesses, hoping—it had to be admitted—Kay's suburban friends would be dazzled and want their own custom-made gold jewelry, but that hadn't happened. Unexpectedly, Kay had chosen a huge ring, cutting even more into their already slim profits.

The neighborhood had gone downhill, Bill raved to Kay over the phone. He needed a gun to bring the trashcan to the curb. Kay understood his concern, but the idea scared her. She tried not to think of the time a masked man waving a gun entered the insurance company and ordered her and her co-workers on the floor. As instructed, she did not look up as he took wallets from purses and pockets, but her recurring nightmares gave the unknown man the face of her brother.

Increasingly, Kay no longer wanted to go into the city, and when she did, she preferred it to be during the day. With her parents both gone, there was no need to visit the house any longer. But when Helen, a good though unconventional sister, invited Kay to her poetry readings, besides not liking to tell Helen no, Kay jumped at any excuse to leave the house. She enjoyed the mild flirtations with Helen's male friends; she preferred the Sunday afternoon readings at the Maple Leaf Bar to the evenings at Borsodi's Coffee House, though next week Kay had promised to go to the latter for a performance of songs Helen had written.

Parking on Oak Street was limited, so she liked to get there early. She pulled in front of the old house to pick up Helen and honked the horn. The last time she'd been inside, Helen's two plump cats roamed the kitchen counters and the smell of cat urine was overpowering. Kay supposed Helen no longer noticed the stench.

Though it was a brisk, sunny afternoon, the bar was dark and dank inside. Whiffs of mildew reached her before she got through the doorway. Kay ignored the man sprawled across the counter, his butt barely on the stool. She was told he was harmless, a sort of mascot or patron saint of the place. Helen had let the man in her house, let him use the shower. Kay skirted around him, her pantsuit almost grazing the wall; he smelled as if he could use a shower now. She wouldn't have been surprised to see flies buzzing around his beard. Helen had said he was not only a poet but a respected university professor as well—which Kay found hard to believe—out of a job due to his drinking—which she didn't find hard to believe.

According to Helen, the readings here were famous, attracting influential poets from all over the country, all over the world. Kay would have to take her at her word for that. It didn't always sound like poetry. One night, Helen read a too-confessional prose piece that enflamed Kay's cheeks and made her want to crawl under her chair. Another time Helen read poems written in Polish and Russian. Kay didn't understand the point of that. Helen could've been spouting gibberish for all anyone else knew. Kay enjoyed the time they read poetry by Kipling and Housman—poetry "to drink by," Helen and her friends called it—though they never needed an excuse for that.

Kay ordered a glass of white wine for herself and the usual for Helen, while Helen meandered toward the courtyard to set up, chatting along the way with the regulars. Not for the first time, it occurred to Kay that Helen invited her so she would pay for her drinks; she was grateful Helen had at least switched from Black to White Russians. She was also grateful that Bill and Beryl had moved eighty miles away. Perhaps Bill would stop his nefarious dealings, or at least she'd no longer have to hear about them. She felt sorry for Bill; so many of his ideas had been brilliant but had not come to fruition—or as with his Mardi Gras floats, bad luck had ruined them. He hadn't been paid for that work, and Kay didn't know where the money for the materials had come from in the first place.

The buzz of the portable microphone interrupted her musing. When the audience members laughed or nodded, she was at a loss, but she'd learned to put on a listening face and to smile when they chuckled. She felt overdressed in her bright matching pantsuit and with her hair sprayed, but shorts or jeans or T-shirts were things she never wore outside the house. Helen didn't wear shorts or jeans either, but her pieces were always mismatched—today's outfit included orange stripes and blue plaid—and Kay had no idea where they'd come from. Helen had the same shape as Mother, tall and thin, but Mother had owned sedate dresses exclusively.

Kay sipped her chardonnay. She looked around: Had she sighed out loud? On the day of her high-school graduation, Mother had discovered that the graduates had escaped to Pat O'Brien's; she'd taken a cab to the French Quarter, told the driver to wait, and plucked Kay from the piano bar. Kay's Hurricane was left unfinished on a table; she'd managed only a few sips—she hadn't liked its sticky-sweetness—but the humiliation of being taken away in front of friends was enough to make anyone cry. She waited till she got home to do so; appearances needed to be kept up, even in front of a taxi driver.

HELEN rested by the light of the moon, next to the old fig tree, her feet on the other chair. Tomorrow she'd leave the house she'd lived in all her life, at least in all her memory of life, to a rented upper flat not far away—from Plum to Sycamore, fruit to shade. She'd survived Bill and Beryl, but she couldn't survive the lien on the house.

She'd have to shoehorn into the new place the paintings she hadn't sold or given away, as well as her boxes of manuscripts. She wouldn't move her old typewriter; Kay had given her the money for a new word processor and a printer. Helen stubbed out her cigarette and pushed her body, achy from packing, away from the table. Henry curled around her legs, only detangling himself when she put one foot in front of the other. He scampered up the steps ahead of her and waited while she opened the screen door. Inside, she locked the back door for the last time and went to bed.

29

THE STORY OF MY MOTHER being whisked away from Pat O'Brien's by my grandmother was told to us often. Mama used it as an example of why she'd vowed to be a different kind of mother than her own. It was only much later that I had sympathy for Grandma Toye. She must have wanted to make sure her "normal," shy, biddable daughter wouldn't turn into an alcoholic like my grandfather.

The *Times-Picayune* archives reveal the foreclosure of the Annunciation Street address and multiple small claims court cases with either Bill's or Beryl's name attached. Though I didn't know about their legal issues at the time, I'm sure my uncle would have asked for my dad's help and that after a while Bill would have been told nothing more could be done for him.

After losing the house, it seems Bill and Beryl tried to survive in New Orleans for a time. Judging by newspaper accounts, they were in New Orleans until at least 1992. I found various articles, mostly by the aforementioned *On the Scene* columnist Frank Gagnard, that document Bill's reincorporation in 1991 of his chamber orchestra which "never got off the drawing board" the first time. He revised the charter and named the projected performance-group the New Orleans Philharmonia. Though still called Bill in the article, he now goes by W. Geoffrey Toye—as well as in an article about receiving an award for taking care of some "homeless" cats. Gagnard's article of October 6, 1991, announcing the "new start" of Bill's group, states that Bill studied music privately, including an "extensive seminar" with conductor William Steinberg. But instead of a projected concert by a projected orchestra, the performance is turned into a solo recital by renowned pianist Susan Starr. (The entertainment section of the *Times-Picayune* of February 9, 1992, notes that Starr's debut in New Orleans, as a child, was under the direction of Alexander Hilsberg, the conductor Bill claimed to have been trained by.) The announced five-concert series by Bill's Philharmonia never happened.

In Gagnard's article of August 9, 1992, Bill is given credit as the spon-
sor of Starr's "artistically successful recital" on that year's Valentine's Day,
perhaps implying it wasn't a monetary success. Gagnard writes of Bill's
focus now being on the formation of a new group, Savoyards of New
Orleans, dedicated to Gilbert and Sullivan operettas. Gagnard quotes
from a press release that says Bill is related to the D'Oyly Cartes, though
distantly, and that "conductor and composer" Geoffrey Toye was Bill's
"uncle and namesake." Poor Mr. Gagnard: He must've been constantly
badgered by Bill and likely didn't believe his press releases' claims.

The *Garden & Gun* article states that Bill and Beryl moved from New
Orleans to Baton Rouge in 1994, though he'd presented himself to prospective Clementine Hunter buyers as a Hurricane Katrina evacuee. Had
they used up all their opportunities in New Orleans? Did they move
to Baton Rouge to take advantage of the Clementine Hunter market?
Tom Whitehead, Hunter friend and biographer, thinks so. In one of the
newspaper articles about the plea deals, he says Baton Rouge might not
be a market for Renoirs, but it was for Clementine Hunters. Her work
is popular in the area.[10]

After Bill and Beryl moved to Baton Rouge, I didn't see them again. I
didn't hear much about them either, only Mama's casual mentions of occa-
sional telephone calls. Bill phoned when he needed something, persisting
until the well of sympathy ran dry. He chewed up his siblings until there
was nothing left; a bone gnawed by a dog wouldn't have been left cleaner.
When the calls stopped, Mama would've been relieved. An invitation
to my second wedding in 1999 was sent to their house on Keaty Drive,
but we heard nothing back. It was like flinging something into a void.

Unlike Bill and Beryl, Helen was evacuated from New Orleans, hit hard
by the aftereffects of the levee breaches days after Hurricane Katrina had
passed. She was still living in the Carrollton neighborhood, on Sycamore,
and was rescued from her elevated home by two men in a boat, one of
whom took her to Abbeville to his relatives. From Houston, where we
were staying in my stepson's small apartment, Tom and I drove to the
Texas-Louisiana border to pick her up from the good Samaritans. Back
in Houston, after having a hearty meal with Aunt Helen and buying her
some necessities, we took her to the airport. She went to my brother
Kevin's house in Memphis, where Mama was staying. At some point
after Helen returned to her New Orleans home, she was scammed by

a couple she let live with her. She ended up in the hospital, her mental illness triggered after years of lying dormant. Her last days were spent in a public nursing home, her mental state stabilized. From before the time of her Katrina rescue, both of her knees were bad and she had trouble walking. She used a wheelchair. She then developed an aggressive form of breast cancer. She died in the nursing home, shortly after Mama had been taken to see her in her own wheelchair. Helen had told her sister she could die happy now. My mother thought Helen died from the effects of her oxygen device falling from her nose rather than from the breast cancer that would've eventually killed her; Mama had seen the device slip from Aunt Helen's nostrils several times during their visit.

30

Such an odd character they thought him, forgetting . . . that characters are
encouraged at the cost of their families' destruction.
—Elizabeth Taylor

I STILL WONDER OVER NOT HEARING of the FBI raid and arrest at the time they happened. In September of 2009, Mama had been living with me for over six months and I no longer had time for the newspaper. I was her full-time caretaker, excepting the tremendous amount of help from my brother Ted when he came to my home to oversee her exercises or take her to doctors' appointments. If Mama received a phone call about her brother while she was living with me, I didn't hear about it.

At the 2012 Louisiana Book Festival at the State Capitol in Baton Rouge, Tom Whitehead spoke on his new book about Clementine Hunter. Still feeling too emotional about my uncle's crimes to listen to Whitehead, I sent my husband to attend the session while I went to a talk on Dickens. Afterward, as we walked into the crisp afternoon, my husband said almost the whole of Whitehead's talk had been about Bill. He told me how Whitehead had pointed toward where the Toyes were living, how he said they'd gotten off "scot-free," living unpunished in a nursing home on such-and-such a road. I read the cramped notes my husband had taken on a small piece of paper, but there was nothing that hadn't already been discussed in the articles I'd seen. We checked out the Whitehead book from the library and read its last chapter; my husband said it had all been in his talk.

I'd picked up the Whitehead book once before, at the LSU Museum of Art in Baton Rouge during a Clementine Hunter exhibit. I returned the book to the rack with shaking hands after noticing the last chapter's title, "Fakes, Forgeries, and the FBI." My husband and I were the only people viewing the exhibit, but I barely spoke. And when I did—to point out something to him or respond to something he'd pointed out to me—it was in hushed tones. I walked around warily, almost feeling guilty, as though if the young man behind the counter knew I was related to the forger, he would ask me to leave.

I looked online for the name of the exhibit: It was called *Louisiana's Artist: Clementine Hunter*. The biography, *Clementine Hunter: Her Life and Art*, by Art Shiver and Tom Whitehead, published by LSU Press, is mentioned concurrently and prominently.[11] Forgeries and forgers are not mentioned at all on the museum's blog post, and I started to doubt my memory of seeing Bill's forgeries at the exhibit. But my husband also remembers them being displayed next to Hunter's paintings for comparison, along with some explanatory information. I remember that too—captions saying the fakes were on loan from the FBI, as was Bill's palette. In a lengthy feature article about the book and the exhibit in *The Advocate*, Hunter's palette is the only one described. The piece says nothing about any forgeries being shown.

Maybe the forgeries were added to the exhibit after the publicity notices were already posted; maybe they were purposely not advertised, the museum not wanting them to be the focus. Maybe Tom and I thought we were going to see only a Hunter exhibit, not realizing it would also include the forgeries, and that was the cause of my unsteadiness. I doubt both of us misremembered, separately, the presence of the forgeries, but I can't verify our memories. I didn't take notes; I didn't even think of taking notes. In 2012, though I'd already written about my mother's family in a fictionalized form, I didn't think I'd be writing about this.

At some point we revisited the Hunter paintings at the Ogden Museum of Southern Art in New Orleans, now part of their permanent collection—paintings I skimmed on previous visits. I focused on the painted figures' eyes; the differences between those in the Hunter paintings and those of the forgeries had been described by Whitehead. We'd read elsewhere of Bill's overuse of pink paint as opposed to Hunter's use of it, another detail that had betrayed him. At the Ogden, Tom pointed out the amount of pink in one of the paintings, trying to lighten my mood by implying that the painting could've been Bill's. Instead, I felt more nervous over the joke, wondering what if it were true.

After writing of the Baton Rouge exhibit, while searching for its official name, I stumble upon a Facebook page titled "Justice for Clementine." Nothing much has been posted there since 2012, and it's not as hard to read of the understandable vitriol now, but some of the language of the outraged commenters about the "innocent Robert" Lucky (perhaps they were his friends; many, if not all, seem to be from Natchitoches, where Lucky was also from) being jailed instead of the Toyes is jarring. I stop writing for a while and think that perhaps my mother was right about hiding the familial relationship.

ON a lazy Sunday evening in 2018, I'm scrolling through Twitter and stop at the sight of a familiar style of painting. A lede blares, "Clementine Hunter and the FBI's Investigation of William J. Toye." I feel shock, once again, coming across his name like that, though I could search online for it at any time. A lecture is being held on Wednesday in Lafayette, Louisiana, two hours from my home. The presentation likely won't hold much information I don't know, but I tell myself I need to hear Randy Deaton—the FBI agent who arrested my uncle—in person. Tom has work, and except for his being with me, I want to go alone, so as to have no outside distractions. It's my way of focusing, of overpowering the anxiety I already feel, something I rarely speak of until whatever has triggered it is over.

To be as steady as possible, I need to follow my routine—eat dinner at my usual time, for example—even though I'm away from home. More than once I've wondered if my mild anxiety and obsessive-compulsive tendencies (my son once remarked that I was OC but didn't have the D) are inherited. If so, I got the good end of the stick; it's manageable. The friend I'm staying with recommends the Blue Dog Café for local flavor, as well as for its being across the street from the University of Louisiana at Lafayette. The Paul and Lulu Hilliard University Art Museum, the site of the lecture, is on campus.

Temperatures are chilly for Louisiana in mid-November, almost freezing. It's been dreary all day; the only hint of sunshine came as I approached Lafayette that afternoon—a bleak wash of sun greeting me, not enough to pull out my sunglasses.

I get to the Blue Dog about ten minutes before 5 p.m. and stand inside the side door; no one notices me, or if they do, I'm ignored. I barely register the Rodrigue paintings of blue dogs along the walls. When I'd googled Deaton, I'd seen that he'd spoken in New Orleans at a fundraising dinner for the George Rodrigue Foundation of the Arts earlier in the year. Not surprisingly, Rodrigue paintings are also a target of forgers.

I walk past tables—some holding customers, others empty. At the hostess stand in the middle of the room, the young woman tells me dinner starts at 5 p.m., and I can sit at the bar, where there will be full service then. Feeling awkward, I return the way I came. Everyone else seems to be a regular or at least to know unwritten rules that I don't. I sit on the one empty barstool, order a beer, and ask for the menu. Hampered by patrons on both sides, I don't pull out the book in my purse. Instead, I look blankly at my phone, willing my mind not to wander, not to think about what's ahead. I'm not completely successful in tamping down the nervousness I feel rising in my chest, but after finishing my meal, I'm steadier. An older man with a half-full wine glass stands behind me, ready to occupy the stool as I prepare to go.

The Hilliard Museum is a modern, sleek building, glass from top to bottom. It's brightly lit. Otherwise, all is in darkness, including the small parking lot at its side. Except for the handicapped spots, there's only one empty slot and I pull my vehicle into it. Scarf around my neck and notebook in my purse, I walk down the sidewalk toward the museum. An older woman bundled against the cold—wearing a big knit cap and bulky knit scarf—approaches me and asks if I'm going to the talk. She asks other questions I can't answer and I tell her I'm not from around here, that I heard of the presentation and thought it sounded interesting. At the front desk we're told the talk is on the second floor, and we go our separate ways.

With twenty minutes to spare, I view the Dali exhibition that will close in a few months, illustrations to accompany *Les Chants de Maldoror*, a long prose poem written by the Comte de Lautréamont, and other illustrations Dali had executed for Dante's *The Divine Comedy*. I've read the latter and haven't heard of the former. Some of *The Divine Comedy* prints are familiar to me from the walls of an art gallery on Royal Street in New Orleans. I'm not absorbing most of the art; my nervousness has returned.

I take the stairs to the second floor and hear a rising babble of voices. It sounds like a large cocktail party in a hotel ballroom. When I get to the room, I'm surprised by how many people are sitting in the large space. Later, when my Lafayette friend asks, I try to visualize how many people were in the audience and I guess fifty or sixty; even later, I will wonder if my estimate was low. As I scan the rows of chairs, I feel awkward again, as if I'm late to a party where I know no one and everyone else knows everyone else.

I ask the woman sitting next to an empty chair at the end of the front row if it's saved. She says, in that friendly Southern way, it's for me. As I settle in, taking off my jacket, pulling out my notebook and pen, she asks if I own a Clementine Hunter painting. When I say I don't, she asks why I've come. I must be as naïve as my mother: It dawns on me that many of the people in the room are here because they're concerned about the authenticity of their own Hunter paintings; that's likely what much of the chatter in the room is about too. I give her the same story I gave to the woman outside the museum. I feel obligated to ask if she owns a Hunter. Gesturing to the older woman sitting to her right, she says her mother owns three, as well as a fake bought purposely to hang at her camp, and another of which she's not sure. I picture a friend's camp, a small fishing cabin, built on stilts and decorated with a nautical theme. But this woman's camp could be bigger and more elaborate: a hunting lodge or even a second home on a bayou.

As we talk, more chairs are being set out—a row in front of us and a shorter row to the side, directly across from the elevator. The new chairs quickly fill, and latecomers stand in back. Someone behind me says their group is from Natchitoches. Their drive would have been the same length as mine, and I feel better for making the trip, as if it's not a crazy idea after all.

On a screen in front of the audience is the image of the Department of Justice/FBI logo superimposed over Clementine Hunter paintings—or perhaps they're forgeries. To the right, near the wall farthest from me, are five paintings, each on its own easel. Four look like Hunter's. One looks like a Matisse.

I wonder if I would've come to the presentation if my mother was still alive. If I'd told her ahead of time I was going, she might have tried to talk me out of it. She believed Bill had brought disgrace upon his family and that if people knew of the connection, they'd think poorly of us, as a family. I would've assured her I wasn't going in order to identify myself. Once I'd returned from the talk, she would've wanted to know all about it. Ironically, she didn't like things being kept from her. I would have told her what I learned. I would have answered her questions. I would've been hoping to help break the chain of secrecy, the one that breeds more secrecy and grows unwarranted shame. A bearded man stands in front of us to introduce Special Agent Randy Deaton, who'd been talking and laughing with audience members sitting near the easels. The first man announces this is the last of the Creative Conversations series hosted by the museum for the year. He says Deaton has been in the FBI since 1998; was a member of the New Orleans Joint Terrorism Task Force; is stationed in Alexandria, Louisiana; and is an Art Crime Team member.

Deaton immediately puts the audience at ease, eliciting a collective chuckle with a self-deprecating joke about his height. I'd love to be able to join in with the laughter, but the tension filling my brain and body precludes it. Deaton says he'll be relating a "fascinating but crazy story." His talk is not an official FBI position but his own statement. Describing his Louisiana background, he says he grew up in the Baton Rouge area. He started investigating the Toye case in 2008. He calls it a "kooky investigation"; the adjective is one he'll use again. Like Dali's melting clocks, the time and situation feel surreal as I prepare to hear the details of the crimes of a notorious criminal, my uncle. Pen hovering above paper, I brace myself and continue taking notes.

On the screen is an article from the April 3, 1974, *Times-Picayune* about the New Orleans Police Department (NOPD) investigating "a guy named William Toye selling Clementine Hunter paintings," Deaton explains. The caption to a grainy photo of two detectives says Toye, 42, was arrested at a "private residence" on Canal Street. Deaton says the address belonged to a Dial-a-Date escort service; the audience laughs. He says Mr. Toye (Deaton always includes the honorifics for Bill and Beryl) sold forgeries from that address; more were found inside his home (he was not living in my grandparents' house at the time), including one in the oven; heat causes a painting to look aged—a detail I'd heard somewhere before. In a detail I don't think I'd heard before, Deaton says Mrs. Toye was on an exercise bike when the detectives arrived, and she remained there the entire visit.

This must have been the same issue that our parents concealed from us the day I came home from school looking for it. I feel haunted by hidden objects and absent people. I think of the occasions when Bill and Beryl weren't there, and I was too young to realize that a physical absence can be felt.

I remember a Thanksgiving at my grandparents' house, Daddy carting in our kiddie-table, its four small chairs, and a high chair for the youngest, through the side door straight into the dining room. The room looked different than usual: the rectangular dining table, with several adult-sized chairs placed around it, had been pulled away from the wall and set with the good dishes. During the tumult of tables and chairs being arranged and rearranged, I silently fretted over where I'd be sitting. I was almost ten years old, and there were six of us children.

Grandma Toye and Mama were flustered, and I was sensitive to any kind of tension. A delicate balance might've been in danger of tipping: the relief of not having to deal with Bill mixed with the knowledge that he could appear unexpectedly. I ruminate on the difficulty of accommodating an erratic family member while protecting young children, which is how my mother would've viewed it—on the real possibility that Mama brought us to our grandparents' home only if she knew Bill wouldn't be there.

The kids' table was placed near the side door by the chifforobe, and I lingered nearby. Food was brought from the tiny kitchen, and finally Aunt Helen told me to sit in one of the empty chairs at the big table, exclaiming I was old enough now. I knew being with the adults wouldn't be as easy, or as fun, as being with my siblings; but I wasn't one to make a fuss, and there was no other choice. Still small for my age, I couldn't reach the table after sitting down. Aunt Helen fetched a telephone directory to boost me up. It was uncomfortable, but I settled in. Uncle Wayne said a prayer of thanksgiving then led us in grace: *Bless us, O Lord* . . .

Deaton clicks to the image of an earlier *Times-Picayune* article from 1969, backtracking to speak of the time Bill reported paintings stolen from his residence. On page two—the prominent location surprises me—among articles that sound as if they could be in today's newspapers, its headline reads, "44 Paintings Are Destroyed." The subheadline states, "6 Others Stolen from Artist's Apt." Deaton doesn't have much to say about this incident, except to point out that the article calls Bill a local artist. The words he leaves unsaid echo my own suspicions that Bill destroyed these paintings himself and that the "stolen" ones never existed. I wonder if my mom had the same reservations. If she did, she likely suppressed them.

Deaton returns quickly to 1974. An image of the General Case Report on William James Toye flashes before my eyes, along with an NOPD photo of four of the forgeries, a few of the many shown to Clementine Hunter. She said they weren't hers. (Is this when she famously wondered why someone would put her name on their picture?) Regardless, the case was dropped, never prosecuted. Deaton doesn't have anything more to say on that, and I've found no explanation. An NOPD detective had said to the paper that their investigation took three months, but perhaps the evidence that Bill had tried to sell his fakes wasn't strong enough and he was given a warning instead. The cry of my aunt's friend reverberates in my head: "They told Bill not to do it again!"

A "bunch of fakes" in the March 8, 1997, catalog of the Louisiana Auction Exchange (LAE) in Baton Rouge prompted an FBI investigation. Deaton says, "Mr. Toye had a thing for Degas," though he thinks Bill's Matisse is his best forgery. The latter adorned the cover of another LAE catalog (thus establishing a fake provenance) and stated "Dr. and Mrs. W. Geoffrey Toye" were its owners. A Jakartan paid $242,000 for the painting, but it never left the United States. After it was deemed a fake, the auction house returned the money to the buyer and the painting to Bill. A photo I've never seen before appears on the screen: A smiling, beguiling "W. Geoffrey Toye" holds a painting claiming to be Matisse's *Fleurs par la fenêtre*. Bill sued his own attorney and the LAE for returning a forgery to him. Deaton chuckles at the gall, and a man in the audience shouts, "He was busy!"

That must mark the end of any recorded Bill-busy-ness for a while, as Deaton then jumps to June 2008, when the FBI opened a mail/wire-fraud criminal investigation, initiated by a victim complaint. He jokes that he got the case because he's the only agent "who watches *Antiques Roadshow*."

The sizes of the forgeries became a question, odd sizes thought to be rare, ones that "commanded a premium." On the screen is displayed, among others, a large painting (created on the back of a mirror) that Robert Lucky, the art dealer convicted of mail fraud in connection with selling fakes attributed to Hunter, called a "tableau," a word Deaton enunciates as if Lucky said it pretentiously. The forgery incorporates multiple known themes of Hunter's.

Mr. Toye isn't the only Hunter forger, says Deaton; there are about five, though not all have been identified. With Bill's paintings, something about the eyes was different than the originals, noticed by those who had "connoisseurship," though Lucky described the paintings as "fabulous" to prospective buyers. The experts also noticed something not right about the signature on paintings starting from 1999. In addition, it was "odd" that so many Christmas tree scenes, supposedly rare, appeared around Christmastime in 1999 and 2000.

In 2005 someone sent their Hunter paintings to a private lab: Two were certified authentic—the other two, forgeries. Without further explanation, Deaton says, "Mr. Toye liked to paint that pink," and I recall Tom's facetious comment about the large Hunter painting on the wall of the Ogden.

Deaton interviewed only people he knew "would keep their mouths shut" as he prepared to obtain a search warrant. When he first presented his evidence to the judge, the latter refused it, saying it was too detailed—enough for a court case but too much for a warrant. He must've rewritten it to the court's satisfaction, because on September 30, 2009, with the warrant in hand, Deaton and other agents went to Bill and Beryl's home on Keaty Drive in Baton Rouge. The house was the kind that "brings your property value down." The yard was overgrown with weeds; Beryl called it her English garden. She answered the door and called for Bill.

Eighteen is mentioned as the number of cats in the home. "I'm not bashing the Toyes, just telling what I saw," Deaton states before describing how they'd saved buckets of used cat litter. Animal Control couldn't catch all the cats, as some escaped through holes in the drywall. He later heard the wall had to be busted to rescue at least one of the cats. He says it's important to remember that cat hair, and a lot of it, was everywhere.

Confiscated as evidence were letters of provenance, ownership history related to other painters besides Hunter; used-up tubes of paints; a book on authentication process ("he's doing homework," Deaton says); a book on Degas; books on other artists; and hardboard, including the back of what Deaton suspects was a medicine-cabinet door, as there's a hole in the "canvas" where a knob would've been. Slides of these items flash by, as well as those of original art by Bill, more letters, and a storeroom in the back yard. The latter reminds me of the shed at the back of my grandparents' property—the one Uncle Bill built to make and store his balsa-wood model buildings, where he had me poke out the windows and doors after he'd traced their outlines with a utility knife. I continue to wonder if I remember doing this or if I only know the story.

The amount of stuff shown on the screen is overwhelming. The stench from the cat litter had to be sickening. I couldn't have entered such a house of horrors. Like Bill, my parents were born during the Great Depression.

My dad picked up washers from the ground, flat metal disks with holes in their centers, and added them to a big glass jar in his crowded utility room, saying you never knew what size you might need when you needed one. He saved cords from old lamps for the same reason. My mother shoved paper and plastic bags from stores under the kitchen sink and in the bathroom closet. Both of my parents thought any kind of paperwork should be kept forever, but none of their behavior rose to the level of keeping used cat litter. I don't know if this hoarding was another sign of a mental disorder for Bill and Beryl, but I find it likely. Their mental-health issues also feel overwhelming.

Another photo zooms in on a desk drawer crammed with various items, a superimposed circle around a typewriter cartridge. Later Deaton says that out of forty documents submitted for analysis, twenty-one suspect letters of provenance were found to be typed with a style of font this cartridge contains, a style not available during the time the letters are dated. I'm reminded of the kind of detective work one might find in Sherlock Holmes stories, or in the stories I used to read in the *Ellery Queen* magazines Mama passed on to Grandpa Toye.

Also inside the drawer are digital-camera memory cards with "pictures after pictures of cats: Smokey, Blackie, Socks, *Minou*." Deaton mentions that Bill liked to paint portraits of cats. Uncle Bill wasn't allowed painting supplies in the nursing home, but he must've been allowed to keep his own paintings. During their visit, my brothers Paul and Michael saw several paintings of cats lined on the walls of Bill and Beryl's room.

Deaton stops at a photo of a colorful abstract on a wall, a Juan Gris forgery, one of the works offered for sale through the LAE. Socks the cat is sprawled on top of a file cabinet beneath the painting. The cat's black body is much larger than the surface it sits upon, and its tail is as long as a drawer and a half. A white paw extends toward a nearby door, as if it's trying to reach the doorknob but is too lazy to get up and turn it. Under the terms of the search warrant, Deaton wasn't allowed to confiscate fine-art forgeries, so the Gris was left behind.

He seized five Clementine Hunter forgeries, four unframed. He gestures toward the latter on the easels to his left: "There they are." Turning back to the screen, he points to the framed forgery, a baptism scene; he says it's now in his office in Alexandria. It was rendered on a green-painted board, instead of green gypsum-board like Hunter used, artificially aged with talcum powder of some sort.

The name and address of the owner of Bill's Matisse forgery was discovered on a document in the Toye house. Deaton motions to the lone painting to his left that's not a Hunter forgery; he says the "Matisse" was given to him by the victim, confiscated as evidence.

The day of the raid, as Bill sat in the agent's air-conditioned car while he stood outside under the sweltering sun, Deaton received two confessions from Bill: the first that his wife made the forgeries; the second that Bill had. Judging from a detailed wide-ruled notebook Bill had labeled "Volume One," the "magic number" of forgeries he created is perhaps 438 as of January 2007. Forgeries are still popping up.

The Toyes claimed they had "this great, massive Clementine Hunter art collection," Deaton says, because Beryl had bought hundreds of paintings from Hunter herself. None were listed in their assets the four times they filed for bankruptcy, which in itself is a federal crime.

Deaton mentions that Bill appeared on Baton Rouge's WAFB Channel 9 local news and declared he was innocent. "Let the grand jury indict," he said, though he'd already been indicted. I'd thought my mom's belief about news of her brother not making its way from Baton Rouge to New Orleans was naive, but she was correct in that we were insulated, at least to a certain extent, from the ordeal. I knew nothing of this interview, and I still wonder when news of his indictment would have come to me if I hadn't seen the newspaper that February morning in 2010.

For a "laundry list" of reasons, including differing signatures and dirt on the suspected forgeries—artificially "aging" paintings by rubbing dirt on them is a known forgery technique—an analytic laboratory deemed one set of paintings unlike the other. Another company discovered electric-sanding marks on the boards the forgeries were painted on and identified the type of sander that made the marks: It was the same type Deaton had found in the Toye home. Also found, embedded in the paint, was cat hair.

In June of 2011 Bill pleaded guilty to one charge of conspiracy. Deaton says what a lot of people don't know about this "crazy, kooky story" is the judge released Bill on his own recognizance with the caveat that he couldn't commit further crimes. Immediately after the trial, on the steps of the federal courthouse, Bill moves fast, going after the *New York Times* photographer with his cane, "swinging for the fence"; he "connects" with the man's expensive camera: "Basically a felony assault." Deaton tells Bill's defense attorney (a "super-nice guy in Lafayette") he didn't see it. Displayed on the screen is the newspaper's close-up of Bill brandishing his cane, a photograph I've seen before and would find hard to forget. When I saw it the first time online, I was shaken to my core, a visceral reaction to the reality of Uncle Bill's offenses.[12] Deaton says that Bill didn't fulfill the court's stipulation of assisting in the identification and cataloging of any Hunter forgery created by him, though he also says he brought about forty forgeries to the nursing home for Bill to sign with his own name, another stipulation of his sentencing. Deaton adds that Beryl "didn't like me at all. Mr. Toye, I thought, liked me." If Deaton listened to Bill's stories, as he must've, I have no doubt my uncle liked him.

While double-checking a fact with my brother Michael about his nursing-home visit to Bill and Beryl, he's unsure of the detail I'm asking about, not only because it's been several years, but also because the couple is "weird," he says. In my family, calling somebody or something weird is normally a compliment, but not this time. Bill's narcissistic weirdness would've added to the strain of attempted communication; to the struggle of focusing on understanding the incomprehensible, affecting the memory of a stressful time.

Take away the romanticized myth of an art forger, a creator churning out reproductions that fool experts. Take away the delusions of a man who spun a dramatic life from credible fragments. Take away the illusions that mask the boring and ugly details of any life. Take it all away and we're left with a man who might be interesting to read and to write about, but one who is wearying to deal with on the quotidian level.

Deaton believes "justice was served," though it took three tries. The case was unique in that it dealt with folk, as opposed to fine, art. Quoting the former director of a folk-art museum, he adds that the FBI investigation had a part in "legitimizing" folk art. Another "unique" thing about the case was Bill's using an art conservator's condition reports to "legitimize" the forgeries, something Deaton says he'll remember for "next time." It was a "long and kind of a kooky" investigation, he concludes, but it was worth it to protect a Louisiana artist and her legacy.

Repulsed by my uncle's actions, I am in complete agreement with

Deaton's last words. No one's work should be misappropriated in such ways, and it feels especially egregious in relation to Clementine Hunter who, due to the policies of the segregated South, lived in near-poverty almost her whole life. I don't know if her art even made her much money during her later years. I remember reading she bought a house trailer with her earnings in 1977, the first and last home she owned.

Deaton asks for questions and, in response to one, says he found Bill's own work on the internet, Storyville paintings and drawings: "The man had talent." I've looked online multiple times, before this presentation and since, and haven't found them. After Aunt Helen went into a nursing home, I discovered one of Uncle Bill's paintings among several of hers. It looks like the St. Augustine, Florida, lighthouse; it's nothing special, but I kept it.

A little boy asks, "Are the cats still alive?" Deaton smiles wryly and answers diplomatically, saying the cats "are no longer with us." Later the same boy asks what happened to the house. Deaton's answer is that it was bought and renovated and now "looks livable."

I wasn't planning on asking a question, but ever since Deaton said the paintings on the easels were Bill's work, one keeps bubbling in my mind. After several questions from others, I raise my hand and ask who owns the forgeries. Deaton answers that these four, and another too bulky to carry around, were seized as evidence, formally forfeited by William Toye at his sentencing, and given to the FBI by the court. They're FBI property, no longer considered evidence because he travels with them to presentations like this one. He's had them converted to "training aids."

As he's answering my question, he plucks a painting off its easel, walks over, and gives it to me, saying something about "how often are you going to get handed a William Toye." Time feels wobbly again, the surreality of my situation intensifying. I came to the talk with no preconceptions as to an outcome, but I almost feel as if a dream-pencil appeared in my hand and I drew these happenings. My mind churns with all the things I could say. I think of Uncle Bill's lighthouse on the wall of my home. I think of myself as a toddler sitting on Uncle Bill's lap, as his forgery is now sitting on mine.

In the foreground of the forgery on my lap is a blue-clad woman holding the leash of an oversized chicken harnessed to a cart full of flowers. In the background a man wearing a red cap pulls another flower cart. I use my phone to take a picture of the painting. A museum photographer rushes over and gets in position to take a photo of me holding the painting. I immediately hand it to the woman sitting to my right as Deaton said it could be passed around.

I'm relieved to have the painting out of my possession so the photographer would move on. I'm not sure why, except that I feel illegal in some way. No one there knew who I was, but my first thought when the first photo of my uncle flashed on the screen was to wonder if anyone would notice a resemblance between him and me. I used to think I looked more like my dad's side of the family, but recently I was starting to see my mom's side in the mirror.

In response to another question, Deaton says some victims wouldn't cooperate with the investigation. He doesn't elaborate. Someone asks if the scheme was just about money. Deaton speculates that any money the Toyes got went to the needs of their cats, as the couple had no money at the time of their arrests.

I feel for these victims—not only for the money they've lost, but also because of the distress they've undergone. As a victim of fraud, one can feel embarrassed that they should have known better than to be duped, even while rationally knowing they've done nothing wrong. Most people want to believe someone is telling the truth, until they're shown differently. I don't know any specific stories of my mother being scammed out of money by her older brother, but it's likely. And not wanting to admit she'd been manipulated by him for much of her life, when all she'd wanted to do was help a loved one, she had another reason to keep his crimes secret from her children.

After Bill's phone calls and requests for help ceased, Mama might have reflected on her past relationship with him and wondered how someone who supposedly loved her could take such advantage of her. At some point, Bill's mental-health issues could not be an excuse for the way he treated people, especially when considering his calculated deceptions. My mother might've concluded that perhaps Bill was incapable of love. That could have been enough for her to consider the matter over with: She was done thinking about it. Someone else asks if the Toyes have any children. Deaton says he's not aware of any. The urge is there for me to answer, but I can only envision the unwanted attention, and curiosity, trained on me if I do, so I don't. Propriety may have been behind Mama's

silence; but I think my childhood shyness, perhaps born from puzzle-
ment over what should or should not be shared—even with other family
members—is behind mine.

At the end of the question-and-answer session Deaton emphasizes,
again, that the Toye case was victim-driven. He encourages anyone who
thinks they might be a victim of a forgery to contact the authorities.
Several people had left at various junctures during the Q&A period; a
few linger behind for last words with Deaton; others wait for the elevator. The presentation lasted two hours and, though it's only 8 p.m., I feel
fatigue setting in.

As I walk down the stairs to the main floor, I hear some men in front
of me developing a theory of why Bill and Lucky did what they did.
They're elaborating from theories discussed in the Q&A. "I bet it started
off innocently," says one. He must be referring to Lucky; I doubt anyone
could believe that of my uncle—I don't. The same man, or maybe one
he's with, says "he" must've then realized they could make money off
it. The rest of their words are lost to me as they reach the bottom of the
stairway and the open ground floor.

I put my jacket on and leave the building. I'm confused in the dark.
The only lights are those of the museum at my back and those playing
upon a water-ripple wall I don't remember seeing when I arrived. People
are crossing a street to my right—I know I didn't arrive from that direction—and I follow two women walking the other way. Unaware of my
presence, they are chatting about the beauty of the museum. I'm grateful
to hear words that are not about my uncle. I discover they're parked in
the same lot I am, and I don't understand how I became disoriented in
such a small space, or why I feel as if my car has been moved from where
I was sure I'd parked it.

Back at my friend's place, I'm restless—not a state I'm used to feeling.
I don't feel capable of looking at my notes or photos yet. After taking a
shower, I watch old TV—episodes of *Perry Mason* and *The Twilight Zone*,
something I never do at home. I'd tried to read but, unusually for me, that
turned out to be impossible. When I've had enough of the TV, I get in
bed with a slim volume of Virginia Woolf's short stories. I've read only
a few pages when I turn out the light around 1 a.m.

My brain stays active as I sleep lightly. I'm cold and I turn up the heat.
I get hot and I turn it down. In the weak morning light, I decide to give

up trying to rest. Waiting to warm up, I answer some texts in bed before putting my socked feet on the bare floor. I press play on the Talking Heads' *Little Creatures* album on my phone and boil some water for the teabags I've brought from home. I pour a pack of oatmeal into a bowl.

When my friend is available to talk, right as "Creatures of Love" is playing, we discuss the presentation. She expresses mild indignation, likely for my benefit and to tease out how I feel, asking if Deaton threw my uncle under the proverbial bus. I say, as I've said to others, I know Bill did wrong, an extreme wrong. When I first read of all he'd done, I was horrified and felt I had to remind myself he hadn't committed murder; but the rationalization was for my sake, to be able to get past my shock. Back then I was bothered that Bill was portrayed as a man whose only relatives were a wife and parents, and that the latter were identified merely as an alcoholic father and a mother's first name. Whenever I search my uncle's name on the internet, whether it's Wikipedia or some other biographical site, seeing the names of his parents—my grandparents—makes me sad, to have them connected to a story like his and known for that reason only—as if being his parents were the only reason for their existence. My grandparents were moral people, good Catholics, struggling to provide for their family. I'm sure they were appalled by the actions (what they knew of them) of their brilliant oldest child.

News articles don't need to report on family members, but what about the feature stories, those wanting to paint a portrait of Bill? They include the drunken father but no other family details. Are those of interest? Are any of those exculpatory? Probably not to the last; but as a reader of human nature, I hope they are more than of prurient interest—that perhaps they are illuminating.

31

Beryl's claim that she'd gone to Melrose and bought paintings from Hunter herself was likely bogus. I doubt she ever stepped foot on the plantation. Months after Deaton's talk, Tom and I visit the area. The night before, I'd banged my toe on a bedside stepstool in our room in a Natchitoches bed and breakfast. The toe is swollen and bruised, and I hobble around the grounds of Melrose Plantation. I joke that Clementine Hunter knows who I'm related to and had caused the injury; at the same time, if I'd believed in spirits, I know Hunter would be a benign one.

Once we pay our entrance fees, we're allowed to wander the grounds before the tour begins. Immediately, we head toward Hunter's cabin. The ground is squishy from an overnight downpour and, not realizing I'm not on packed grass, my injured foot descends into the slop. I stop in pain.

When I'm finally inside Hunter's little white house, I view the exhibits on the wall charting the history of her developing talent and her evolving signature. A caption under a photo of *Two Ladies in Masks and Man Hunting Birds* says Hunter "never hesitated to mingle images and themes." A reproduction of *Chicken Pulling Flower Cart* reminds me of the forgery I held in my lap. The caption for an image of a painting called *Courtroom*—a theme of hers unknown to me—reads, "Lawyers and judges often collected these paintings." Though it wasn't described in the article I'd read, a Toye forgery was said to have hung briefly in Louisiana lawyer, then–U.S. Senator David Vitter's office. I guess it was taken down once his Hunter was discovered to be a fake.

The guided tour takes us inside the African House to the second floor where Hunter's impressive murals are kept. I don't have trouble going up the stairs, but the pain is excruciating coming down, so I opt to skip the second story of the main house where a Hunter quilt adorns a bed. No photography is allowed in either building. As we leave the grounds, Tom describes the quilt, created from cloth strips, and repeats what the guide said about the rarity of Hunter's quilts.

We drive to nearby St. Augustine Church and its cemetery. I stay in the car to save my foot, as Tom searches for Hunter's grave. It doesn't take him long to find it, a white mausoleum in the back to the right. I walk toward it and snap a few photos. Someone has placed three roses—one small and white, the others larger and pink—above her initials, which are inscribed in the same way she signed her later paintings. It's a simple, sweet, touching memorial. I've kept a photo of it on my phone. She lived to be 101 years old.

32

Shortly after pleading not guilty to four counts of mail fraud and conspiracy to commit mail fraud, Bill and Beryl pleaded guilty to one count of conspiracy. The other charges were dismissed in a plea agreement. The Toyes were sentenced to two years of probation in late 2011 and ordered to pay $426,393 in restitution, which they never paid. Beryl was also sentenced to a year of in-home confinement—an intriguing detail, as I don't know why the judge found that necessary for her and not for Bill. Their ages and their health likely played a role in their avoiding jail time.

They lived out the rest of their lives in an assisted-living facility in Baton Rouge. I'd contemplated making a visit, but whenever I thought of even having to search for the name and address of the nursing home, I developed a persistent headache. I urged myself to toughen up, but I felt any energy I had for visiting a housebound relative should be directed toward my mom. Knowing a visit to my aunt and uncle would make me anxious, uncomfortable, and would be tiresome—though that was the least of my worries—I felt like a coward.

I didn't know of their plans beforehand, but when Paul and Michael visited the couple about a year or so after their sentencing, I became content that at least someone had seen them. When my brothers told Mama and me about their visit, they laughed at Beryl's telling them they were princes of Ireland, rolled their eyes at her using a book on Irish history as proof. Uncle Bill told them the story of my poking out the windows and doors of the models he'd created in the shed behind my grandparents' house, still referring to me as Baby Doll. It's probably the only family story he had about any of us children.

One reason for my brothers' visit was to tell Bill of the death of his sister Helen in 2012. Michael visited again in late 2015 and told Uncle Bill of the death of his other sister—our mother, Kay. The news of the deaths seemed to bounce off Bill and Beryl, confirming my belief, and excuse, that any visit by any relative wouldn't mean much to them—except for their being able to spin their stories to someone, as Bill likely did to Agent Deaton. Bill and Beryl lived for only themselves, and perhaps for each other. That they found each other in 1967 was fortuitous for them, though not for others.

33

Aꜰᴛᴇʀ ᴛʜᴇ FBI ᴀɢᴇɴᴛ handed me my uncle's painting, I felt I had come full circle. The story I'd lived through, the story that had been told to me, the story that was repeated by my uncle to my brothers—the story of his instructing me to push out the doors and windows of his models—had led to my holding his forgery on my lap. But we all know a story never ends, not even with a death. Robert Lucky, someone I never knew, died in 2017. My uncle died in early 2018. Beryl died a few years later. Despite the deaths, their deplorable legacy will, to some degree, run alongside the brilliant legacy of Clementine Hunter. As recently as January 29, 2019, I came across a new online story that discusses the Hunter-Toye case and quotes Deaton.[13] Obviously it's still a relevant topic, my uncle's case perhaps being the tip of an iceberg. The harm my uncle and his wife did cannot be erased by the telling of this story. It cannot be lessened. But it is a story. And the telling of it, despite William Toye's sister's—my mother's—best efforts, continues.

Bill's DNA, perhaps his mental illness, perhaps his brilliance, perhaps his genius, from whomever he inherited those traits, runs through his indirect descendants' cells—though likely to a lesser degree—for both good and bad. In this instance, at least, lesser seems better, as who would choose to live a life like his, driving away those who would've loved him, to live a life of squalor and to die in infamy—though his delusions told him otherwise?

I've written of my shock at the revelation of my uncle's crimes. Another reason for my initial feelings, which included disbelief—a disbelief I still feel in a way and perhaps it's my real reason for writing this, that is, to make it real—is that we're such an ordinary family. My mother's immediate family, albeit including intelligent persons, was nothing extraordinary. Until my uncle's activities became known, there was nothing newsworthy about his—our—family, except perhaps his sister Helen's accomplishments in the arts. She is still remembered by those I meet within the literary community of New Orleans. I consider my family to be commonplace, nothing setting us apart from any other family. We live our lives like thousands of others.

Late in her life, my mother said to me she thought by that time her life would have calmed down; after raising six children, she thought she had earned her measure of peace. I told her life is full of change, that we aren't guaranteed peace, ever. I wished it for her, though. I wish it for all of us.

Epilogue

I'M PONDERING Mama's relationship with Bill, when the memory of a story told to me by their youngest brother leads me down a different path. After my mother's funeral, to illustrate her generosity, Uncle Wayne spoke of her paying for their popcorn from the neighborhood movie theater. Nine years older than Wayne, she'd tell him, "If you're flying, I'm buying," and he'd take off. The story makes me smile—not just at the slang of the time, but because of my mother's love of popcorn.

When we were kids, in preparation for TV events—*Peanuts* holiday specials, *Gone with the Wind*, sometimes just the Friday evening slate of sitcoms—Mama dropped popcorn kernels in vegetable oil at the bottom of her biggest heavy-duty pot, the same one she cooked red gravy in for our twice-a-week pasta dinners, casting the seeds evenly before turning up the gas burner. When the pot clamored for attention and the tantalizing aroma permeated the house, we were drawn to the kitchen as if Mama were the Pied Piper. Bowls were filled with the fluffy salted corn, and we all settled in to watch the show. At a commercial break, I took an empty bowl to the stove for a refill. I helped my youngest brother, nine years younger than me, to more.

The tradition continued with my children. When Rhea and Mage were at my parents' for a babysitting evening, their grandmother made popcorn and put in a VHS tape of one of their favorites, such as the musical film version of *The Little Prince*. My mom sang along to "It's a Hat," the opening tune that's paired with "I Need Air." Afterward, my children acted out the movie, Rhea taking on several roles and Mage, as the little prince, crowning the performance with his tearful exclamation of "And you think that's not important!"

In their adult years, Wayne and my mother were divided by Lake Pontchartrain but never by temperament or by negative feelings. During their frequent phone conversations, Mama would've felt free to express her frustrations over Bill, and Wayne would've responded to her with sympathy and a dose of humor. Mama loved to laugh, and she would have been grateful for the respite, as I am grateful to Uncle Wayne for his story and for the memory that pointed me toward joyous and light-hearted connections between the generations.

Notes

1. (P. xi)   Information about Clementine Hunter was reviewed on Wikipedia and *Encyclopedia Britannica* online and verified by several additional sources. See "Further Reading on Clementine Hunter" (on p. 136) to learn more.

2. (P. 35)   John Ed Bradley, "The Talented Mr. Toye," *Garden & Gun,* April/May 2010.

3. (P. 35)   "Men! Boys: Get in Opera," *Times-Picayune,* October 4, 1949.

4. (P. 41)   Ad in the *Times-Picayune,* April 20, 1949.

5. (P. 41)   "We are Voting for Stevenson because . . . ," *Times-Picayune,* October 30, 1952.

6. (P. 47)   "13 Concert Art Winners Named," *Times-Picayune,* May 31, 1958.

7. (P. 62)   "Background on Candidates Seeking Seats," *Times-Picayune,* November 1, 1965.

8. (P. 79)   *Times-Picayune,* January 15 to January 16, 2006.

9. (P. 101)   "NOMA having a ball with Beaton show," *Times-Picayune,* November 8, 1989.

10. (P. 108)   John Pope, "Clementine Hunter forgers plead guilty after long career selling fake paintings," *Times-Picayune,* August 7, 2011.

11. (P. 112)   "LSU Museum of Art and LSU Press Celebrate Artist Clementine Hunter," LSU Press Blog, https://blog.lsupress.org/lsu-museum-of-art-and-lsu-press-celebrate-artist-clementine-hunter/.

12. (P. 122)   Campbell Robertson, "For a Longtime Forger, Adding One Last Touch," *New York Times,* June 7, 2011.

13. (P. 131)   Margaret Carrigan, "African-American Fakes are on the Rise," *Art Newspaper,* January 4, 2019.

Further Reading on Clementine Hunter

Allured, Janet. "Clementine Hunter." *64 Parishes*, 64parishes.org/entry/clementine-hunter.

Catlin, Roger. "Self-Taught Artist Clementine Hunter Painted the Bold Hues of Southern Life." *Smithsonian Magazine*, October 18, 2018.

Gasperri, Robert. *Clementine Hunter: A Sketchbook* (New Orleans: Ogden Museum of Southern Art, 2014).

Gibson, Jamesha. "Painted Memoir: The Story of Clementine Hunter and the African House Murals." National Trust for Historic Preservation, April 22, 2015. savingplaces.org.

Melrose on the Cane. melroseplantation.org.

Moses, Jennifer. "Looking for Clementine Hunter's Louisiana." *New York Times*, June 14, 2013.

National Trust for Historic Preservation. "African House at Melrose Plantation." savingplaces.org.

Shiver, Art, and Tom Whitehead. *Clementine Hunter: Her Life and Her Art* (Baton Rouge: Louisiana State University Press, 2012).

Acknowledgments

Thank you to my wonderful friends who read and supported this work from its early days: my besties Cathrine Lødøen and Miki Pfeffer, for much more than I could ever express here, including, respectively, the concept and the actualization of an "elsewhere"; friend and mentor Tara Masih, who suggested the title and freely gives of her wisdom and experience; Melinda Palacio, and Susan Larson. I am also grateful for the specific and particular contributions of Constance Adler, Celeste Berteau, Anne Boyd Rioux, Gina Ferrara, Mitch Nodier, and Howard Noble, as well as Pia Ehrhardt and Steph Post. I am beyond thankful to Marie Breaux for the generous gift of her time and expertise.

The biggest of thanks goes to Casie Dodd for providing this book with the best home it could ever have, from its blueprint to the final touches of comforts, and everything in between.

Much love to my family, those mentioned in this book and those not, including my stepchildren and their children. Thank you to my son, who was the first to tell me I should be writing; to my daughter, who promoted even my earliest efforts; and to my husband—without him I would not have all that's necessary for a literal and metaphorical writing-room of my own.

TERESA TUMMINELLO BRADER is a New Orleanian, spurred on to writing by the aftermath of Hurricane Katrina. She has a bachelor of arts in English from Marquette University, her four years in Milwaukee the only time she lived away from the city of her birth. Her short stories, essays, poetry, and reviews can be found at various online literary sites, as well as in print anthologies. This is her first book.

LETTING IN AIR AND LIGHT
was designed, edited, and typeset by
Belle Point Press in Fort Smith, Arkansas.
The text is set in Arno Pro.

The mission of Belle Point Press is to celebrate the
literary culture and community
of the American Mid-South:
all its paradoxes and contradictions,
all the ways it gets us home.
Visit us at
www.bellepointpress.com.

BELLE
POINT
PRESS

Fort Smith, Arkansas